Houghton
Mifflin
Harcourt

MATH 180® COURSE II

S0-AZQ-948

mSpace Volume 2

Printed in the U.S.A.

ISBN 978-0-545-80631-2

18   19   20   21   22   0029   25   24   23   22   21   20

4510007030

Contents Volume 2

BLOCK 5

Proportional Relationships

Imagine That

Pages 2–45B

TOPIC 1	TOPIC 2	TOPIC 3
Representing Proportional Relationships	**Solution Sets**	**Applications of Percent**
Page 4	Page 18	Page 32

PERFORMANCE TASK:
Create a Scaled Mural..........................Page 44

MINDSET STRATEGY:
Reflect on Expanding Mental Capacity .. Page 45A

BLOCK 6

Linear Relationships

On the Money

Pages 46–89B

TOPIC 1	TOPIC 2	TOPIC 3
Linear Equations	**Slope of a Line**	**Interpreting Linear Equations**
Page 48	Page 62	Page 76

PERFORMANCE TASK:
Street Fair Sales ....Page 88

MINDSET STRATEGY:
Reflect on Self-Efficacy....................Page 89A

BLOCK 7

Graphs in the Plane

Make Yourself Heard

Pages 90–133B

TOPIC 1	TOPIC 2	TOPIC 3
Patterns With Negative Numbers	**Negative Slope**	**Operations With Negative Numbers**
Page 92	*Page 106*	*Page 120*

PERFORMANCE TASK:
Compare With Negative Slope .... *Page 132*

MINDSET STRATEGY:
Reflect on Developing Grit .... *Page 133A*

BLOCK 8

Functions

Crack the Code

Pages 134–177B

TOPIC 1	TOPIC 2	TOPIC 3
Representing Functions	**Analyzing Functions**	**Squares and Square Roots**
Page 136	*Page 150*	*Page 164*

PERFORMANCE TASK:
Design a Game Board .... *Page 176*

MINDSET STRATEGY:
Reflect on Learning From Mistakes ..... *Page 177A*

BLOCK 9

Systems of Equations

Take Care

Pages 178–221B

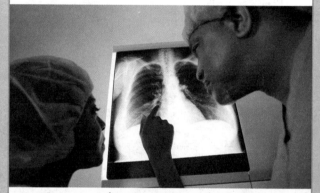

TOPIC 1	TOPIC 2	TOPIC 3
Comparing Linear Functions	**Reasoning With Linear Systems**	**Solutions of Systems**
Page 180	*Page 194*	*Page 208*

PERFORMANCE TASK:
Analyze Fitness Plans....................... *Page 220*

MINDSET STRATEGY:
Reflect on Overcoming Obstacles .... *Page 221A*

Reference Guide .... *Page 223*

Glossary .... *Page 236*

Credits .... *Page 252*

Contents

VOCABULARY

coefficient

collinear points

constant of proportionality

percent

proportional relationship

solution

unit rate

Model City

What does it take to build a city?

Building a tiny city is a big task. In this Anchor Video, see how two brothers teamed up with artists and programmers to build the world's biggest model airport.

Math in Design

In this Block, you will explore how proportional relationships are used in art and design.

Video Game Designers

use **proportional relationships** when designing characters. If a character's foot is $\frac{1}{4}$ **of the length** of her leg, this **ratio** should stay the same when players zoom in or out.

Tailors

use **proportional relationships** when altering clothes. Men usually want pant cuffs to cover between $\frac{2}{3}$ and $\frac{3}{4}$ of the laces on their shoes.

Architects

create **scale drawings** to put their designs on paper. A commonly used **scale** is $\frac{1}{4}$ **inch to 1 foot**. With this scale, a **20-foot-tall** house is only **5 inches tall** on paper.

Interior Designers

make sure the area of carpeted floor in an apartment is about **4 times** the area of uncarpeted floor. This prevents noise from being carried across to other apartments.

Comic Book Artists

have to find a **proportional relationship** between a drawing's height and width so it scales down to a **6-inch-by-9-inch** space.

LESSON 1

Block Preview

> Read the Career Explorations on *mSpace* page 3. Which career interests you the most? Why?

The career that interests me the

most is _____

because _____

_____

_____

> Why is math so important to art and design?

Math is important to art and

design because _____

_____

_____

_____

LESSON 2

Missing Numbers

> Complete the table.

Cans of Spray Paint	Cost ($)
1	3
2	6
4	
	21
10	

> How could you use the cost of 2 cans of spray paint to find the cost of 10 cans?

I could _____

_____

_____

_____

_____

LESSON 3

Who's Right?

> Ava says the person traveled 10 miles in 1 hour. Troy says the person traveled 5 miles in 1 hour.

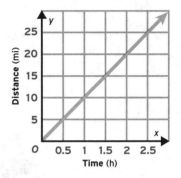

Who's right? _____

> How do you know who is correct?

I know _____ is correct because

_____

_____

_____

_____

_____

Brain Teaser

> **Answer the question.**

- Brian traveled for 3 hours, at a speed of 15 miles per hour.

- Ming traveled for 4 hours, at a speed of 10 miles per hour.

- Jen traveled for 6 hours, at a speed of 5 miles per hour.

Who traveled the farthest?
_____

> **How did you solve the problem?**

I solved the problem by _____

_____

_____

_____

_____

_____

Brain Arcade

> **Use the numbers on the conveyor belt to complete the equations.**

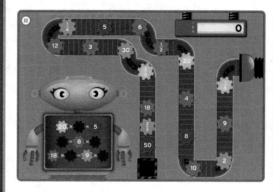

$$20 \times \underline{\hspace{1cm}} = 5$$

$$\underline{\hspace{1cm}} = 8 \times \underline{\hspace{1cm}}$$

$$18 \times \underline{\hspace{1cm}} = 9 \times \underline{\hspace{1cm}}$$

> **How are the given numbers in the third equation related?**

The numbers in the equation are related because _____

_____

_____

_____

_____

_____

> **In this Topic, you learned how to interpret the unit rate of a proportional relationship as the constant of proportionality.**

What does the k-value represent in the equation $y = kx$?

A proportional relationship is represented by the equation $y = kx$, where the k-value is the constant of proportionality. This is also the unit rate between x and y.

LESSON 1
PROBLEM SOLVING

> EXPLORE

ANCHOR VIDEO CONNECTION

As the Anchor Video shows, a scale model maintains the same relationships between all measurements in the original structure.

Design a Scale Model

> You are an urban planner designing a new city park. You completed a scale drawing. But, the city has just asked you to include a new ice rink in your drawing.

The new ice rink measures 36 feet by 36 feet. Modify your drawing to include the new ice rink.

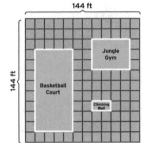

Original Drawing

144 ft

144 ft

Jungle Gym

Basketball Court

Climbing Wall

All park attractions must be at least 12 feet from each other and the outer park perimeter.

A CREATE

Determine the scale for the new drawing. Then, create a new scale drawing that includes all park attractions and the new ice rink.

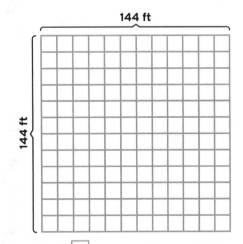

144 ft

144 ft

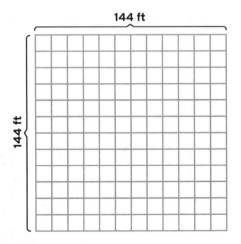

144 ft

144 ft

Each ☐ represents ____ feet by ____ feet.
The ratio of the drawing measurements to the actual measurements is _____.

BIG IDEA **1** Proportional relationships can be represented with tables, graphs, and equations.

BIG IDEA **2** **Modeling a situation with an equation** helps us to find a solution for any value.

EXIT Ticket

B PREDICT

The maximum number of people allowed in a park is 8 people for every unused 12-by-12-foot area. What is the maximum number of people allowed in this park? Explain.

_____

_____

_____

_____

_____

_____

C EXPLAIN

The city wants to add a picnic area that measures 24 feet by 36 feet. Can it fit without removing any of the other park attractions?

_____

_____

_____

_____

_____

_____

> *Select all that apply.*

Analyze the original scale drawing of the park. Which of the statements are true?

☐ The actual dimensions of the basketball court are 96 feet by 48 feet.

☐ The dimensions of the climbing wall are half the dimensions of the jungle gym.

☐ The ratio of the area of the jungle gym to the area of the entire park is 1:12.

☐ The ratio of the area of the jungle gym to the area of the basketball court is 1:12.

Using equivalent ratios can help me to create a scale drawing of a real space.

SCORE ⓪ ① ②

| 0 = Incorrect or No Response |
| 1 = Partial Response |
| 2 = Complete and Accurate |

BLOCK 5

> WORKED EXAMPLE

> TRY IT

> GUIDED LEARNING

Rod is an animator for Space Squirrels, a cartoon about squirrels on a quest for space acorns. The graph shows the time it takes Rod to draw characters. How many characters can he draw in 9 hours?

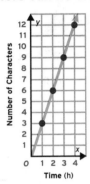

STEP 1 Use the graph to complete the table.

Time (h) x	Process	Characters y
1	1•3 = 3	3
2	2•3 = 6	6
3	3•3 = 9	9
4	4•3 = 12	12

STEP 2 Describe the multiplicative relationship.

STEP 3 Write an equation.

$$x•3 = y$$

STEP 4 Solve the problem.

$$9•3 = 27$$

Rod can draw ___27___ characters in 9 hours.

1

A jewelry designer makes a mold for silver pendants in his collection. The graph shows the weight of silver he needs. How many grams of silver does he need to make 10 pendants?

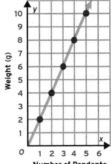

He needs _____ grams of silver to make 10 pendants.

2

Zoe, a video game designer, is creating a video game with zombies. The graph shows the time it takes her to sketch the game levels. How many levels can Zoe sketch in 7 hours?

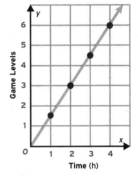

STEP 1 Use the graph to complete the table.

Time (h) x	Process	Game Levels y
1		
2		
3		
4		

STEP 2 Describe the multiplicative relationship.

STEP 3 Write an equation to represent the relationship.

STEP 4 Solve the problem.

Zoe can sketch _____ levels in 7 hours.

> PRACTICE

3 Justin, a hair stylist, is at a styling competition. The graph shows the number of seconds it takes him to braid different lengths of hair. At this rate, what length of hair can Justin braid in 20 seconds?

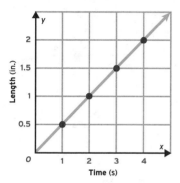

Time (s) x	Process	Length (in.) y
1		
		1
		1.5
4		

Equation:

Justin can braid _____ inches of hair in 20 seconds.

4 A photographer is enlarging his photo of the Eiffel Tower. The graph shows the corresponding heights and widths of the photo. What is the height of a photo with a width of 15 inches?

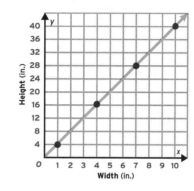

Width (in.) x	Process	Height (in.) y
1		
		16
7		
		40

Equation:

The height of a photo is _____ inches with a width of 15 inches.

EXIT
Ticket

BLOCK
5

TOPIC 3

TOPIC 2

TOPIC 1

> **Solve the problem.**

April needs to buy film for her movie. The table shows the number of minutes that can be put on different lengths of film. What length of film does April need for 11 minutes of her movie?

Time (min) x	Process	Length (cm) y
1		90
2		180
3		270
4		360

April needs _____ centimeters of film for 11 minutes of her movie.

> **Will a 20-minute movie fit on 1500 cm of film? Why or why not?**

A 20-minute movie will / will not fit on 1500 cm of film because

_____

_____

_____

_____

SCORE ⓪ ① ②

| 0 = Incorrect or No Response |
| 1 = Partial Response |
| 2 = Complete and Accurate |

LESSON 3

Interpret Proportional Relationships

BLOCK 5

> **WORKED EXAMPLE**   > **TRY IT**   > **GUIDED LEARNING**

An architect draws a blueprint to scale for a new football stadium. What is the actual distance in the stadium if the distance is 3.5 inches on the blueprint?

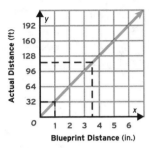

STEP 1 **Make an estimate.**

Estimate: _between 96 ft and 128 ft_

STEP 2 **Find the unit rate.**

Unit rate: __32__ feet per inch

STEP 3 **Express the proportional relationship with an equation.**

$$y = 32 \cdot x$$

STEP 4 **Solve the problem.**

$$y = 32 \cdot 3.5$$
$$y = 112$$

The actual distance in the stadium is __112__ feet if the distance is 3.5 inches on the blueprint.

My answer (is) / is not reasonable because _112 ft is within my_ _estimate of 96 ft and 128 ft._

1

Alan is designing a costume for a play. The graph shows the time it takes him to sew the fabric. What length of fabric can Alan sew in 1.5 minutes?

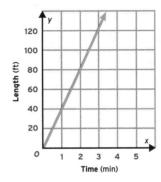

Alan can sew _____ feet of fabric in 1.5 minutes.

2

Jose, a freelance photographer for a New York newspaper, earns money photographing professional baseball games. How much does Jose earn in 5.25 hours?

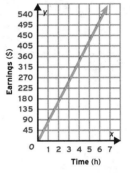

STEP 1 **Make an estimate.**

Estimate: _____

STEP 2 **Find the unit rate.**

Unit rate: $_____ per hour

STEP 3 **Express the proportional relationship with an equation.**

STEP 4 **Solve the problem.**

Jose earns $_____ in 5.25 hours.

My answer is / is not reasonable because _____

_____

---

proportional relationship *(n)* a relationship where values form equivalent ratios

EXIT
Ticket

BLOCK
5

TOPIC 3

TOPIC 2

TOPIC 1

> **PRACTICE**

3

Lea, a fashion designer, is making suits for actors at an awards show. The graph shows the cost of the fabric. What is the cost of 4.5 yards of the fabric?

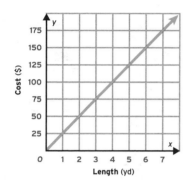

Estimate: _____

Unit rate: $_____ per yard

Equation: _____

The cost of 4.5 yards of the fabric is $_____.

My answer is / is not reasonable because _____

_____

4

An animator is illustrating the character Toby Tornado for a cartoon. The graph shows how fast the character spins. How many times will Toby Tornado spin in 1.9 seconds?

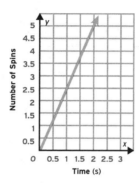

Estimate: _____

Unit rate: _____ spins per second

Equation: _____

Toby Tornado will spin _____ times in 1.9 seconds.

My answer is / is not reasonable because _____

_____

> **Solve the problem.**

Rachel, a graphic designer, styles letters for a magazine. The graph shows the time it takes her to style letters. How many letters does Rachel style in 4.5 minutes?

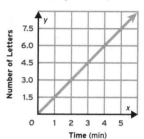

Rachel styles _____ letters in 4.5 minutes.

> **Can you use the same equation to determine how many letters Rachel styles in 20 minutes? Explain.**

I can / cannot use the same equation because _____

_____

_____

_____

_____

_____

SCORE ⓪ ① ② | 0 = Incorrect or No Response
1 = Partial Response
2 = Complete and Accurate

Interpret Constant of Proportionality

> WORKED EXAMPLE

> TRY IT

> GUIDED LEARNING

BLOCK 5

1

2

Alice sketches for a comic book. The table shows the proportional relationship between the time and the number of frames she sketches. How many frames can Alice sketch in 9 hours?

Time (h) x	Frames y
2.5	7.5
5	15
6.5	19.5
9	27

STEP 1 **Make an estimate.**

Estimate: < 30 frames

STEP 2 **Find the constant of proportionality, k.**

$15 \div 5 = 3$

Unit rate: __3__ frames per hour

$k =$ __3__

STEP 3 **Express the proportional relationship with an equation.**

number of frames = k · hours

$y = 3 \cdot x$

STEP 4 **Solve the problem.**

$y = 3 \cdot 9$
$y = 27$

Alice can sketch __27__ frames.

My answer (is)/ is not reasonable because 27 frames < 30 frames.

Dana screen-prints designs on T-shirts for rock concerts. The table shows the proportional relationship between the time and the number of T-shirts she makes. How many T-shirts can Dana make in 8.5 hours?

Time (h) x	T-shirts y
1	4
4.5	18
6	24
8.5	

Dana can make _____ T-shirts in 8.5 hours.

Tony paints hockey masks for goalies. The table shows the proportional relationship between ounces of paint and the cost. What is the cost of 17.5 ounces of paint?

Paint (oz) x	Cost ($) y
3	4.50
8	12
11	16.50
17.5	

STEP 1 **Make an estimate.**

Estimate: _____

STEP 2 **Find the constant of proportionality, k.**

Unit rate: $_____ per ounce

$k =$ _____

STEP 3 **Express the proportional relationship with an equation.**

_____ = ____ · _____

STEP 4 **Solve the problem.**

The cost is $_____.

My answer is / is not reasonable because _____

> PRACTICE

3

Ming prints sonnets and needs to count the lines of text he uses. The table shows the proportional relationship between the sonnets and the number of lines. How many lines of text are used for 53 sonnets?

Sonnets x	Lines of Text y
5	70
21	294
30	420
53	

Estimate: _____

Unit rate: _____ lines of text per sonnet

k = _____

Equation:

_____ = ___ • _____

_____ lines of text are used for 53 sonnets.

My answer is / is not reasonable because _____

4

A jeweler uses links to make a necklace. The table shows the proportional relationship between the number of links and the length of the necklace. What is the length of a necklace with 45 links?

Links x	Length (in.) y
7	5.6
20	16
28	22.4
45	

Estimate: _____

Unit rate: _____ inches per link

k = _____

Equation:

_____ = ___ • _____

The length of a necklace with 45 links is _____ inches.

My answer is / is not reasonable because _____

EXIT Ticket

BLOCK **5**

TOPIC 3

> **Solve the problem.**

David paints a set for a play. The table shows the proportional relationship between gallons of paint and the area of the set. What area of the set can 11 gallons of paint cover?

Paint (gal) x	Area (sq ft) y
2.5	400
4	640
7.5	1200
11	

11 gallons of paint can cover _____ square feet of the set.

> **Marcus needs to paint 500 square feet. Can 3 gallons of paint cover this area? Explain.**

3 gallons of paint can / cannot cover this area, _____

_____

_____

SCORE ⓪ ① ②

| 0 = Incorrect or No Response |
| 1 = Partial Response |
| 2 = Complete and Accurate |

TOPIC 2

TOPIC 1

Develop Proportional Reasoning

RULES

What's My Point? *(Level 1)*

> I think about the relationship of the two numbers when creating an ordered pair. What will the multiplier be?

What You Need
- *mSpace* pages 14–17
- Paper clips
- Pencils

What to Know
- Place paper clip in the center of the spinner. Use the tip of a pencil to hold it in place while spinning.
- One player is X. The other is O. Plot points with these symbols.
- Players may not claim the other player's points.

How to Win
- A player claims a point when the ordered pair is already plotted on the graph.
- The player who claims the most points wins.

> HOW TO PLAY

STEP 1 Spin the spinner for two values: one blue, one yellow.

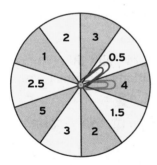

TURN	x	k	EQUATION (y = kx)	(x, y)	POINT CLAIMED
1					
2					

STEP 2 Choose which value will be the *x*- and the *k*-value.

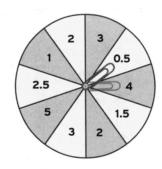

TURN	x	k	EQUATION (y = kx)	(x, y)	POINT CLAIMED
1	0.5	4			
2					

STEP 3 Substitute the values into the equation.

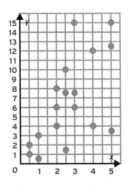

TURN	x	k	EQUATION (y = kx)	(x, y)	POINT CLAIMED
1	0.5	4	y = 4•0.5		
2					

STEP 4 Find the *y*-value, and plot the point. Mark off and claim the point if it is already plotted.

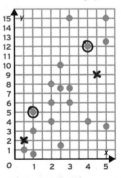

TURN	x	k	EQUATION (y = kx)	(x, y)	POINT CLAIMED
1	0.5	4	y = 4•0.5	(0.5, 2)	yes
2					

RECORDING SHEET
What's My Point?
(Level 1)

> Players share the same recording sheet and graph to plot points.

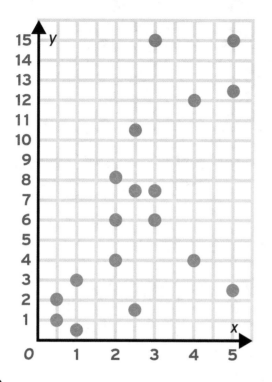

PLAYER A

TURN	k	x	EQUATION (y = kx)	(x, y)	POINT CLAIMED
1					
2					
3					
4					
5					
6					
7					
8					
				TOTAL	

PLAYER B

TURN	k	x	EQUATION (y = kx)	(x, y)	POINT CLAIMED
1					
2					
3					
4					
5					
6					
7					
8					
				TOTAL	

BLOCK 5 > TOPIC 1
LESSON 5
GAME

RECORDING SHEET
What's My Point?
(Level 1)

> Players share the same recording sheet and graph to plot points.

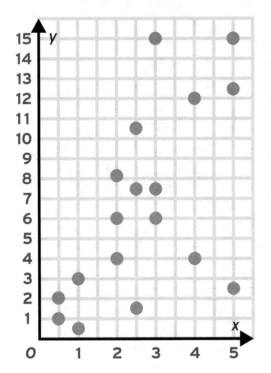

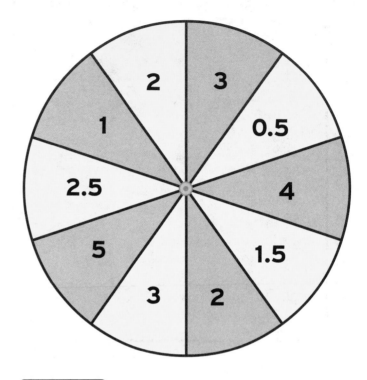

PLAYER A					
TURN	k	x	EQUATION (y = kx)	(x, y)	POINT CLAIMED
1					
2					
3					
4					
5					
6					
7					
8					
				TOTAL	

PLAYER B					
TURN	k	x	EQUATION (y = kx)	(x, y)	POINT CLAIMED
1					
2					
3					
4					
5					
6					
7					
8					
				TOTAL	

INTERIOR DESIGNERS determine how the space inside buildings or the rooms in a house should look. They often use scale drawings and floor plans when decorating a space and choosing furniture that fits.

This scale drawing shows the floor plan of an apartment. The length of each side of a square in the grid represents 12 inches in the actual apartment.

DINING ROOM

LIVING ROOM

BATHROOM

KITCHEN

BEDROOM

CLOSET

> **Using the grid lines in the floor plan, what are the actual dimensions of the living room?**

Length: _____

Width: _____

> **An interior designer selects a sectional sofa to place in the living room. Using the floor plan, shade the space where the sectional sofa could be placed.**

36 in.

108 in.

72 in.

72 in.

36 in.

36 in.

72 in.

144 in.

EXIT Ticket

BLOCK 5

TOPIC 3

TOPIC 2

TOPIC 1

> **Solve the problem.**

Circle the player who found the correct multiplier for the ordered pair (3, 12).

Joy

$$k = \frac{4}{12}$$

Ben

$$k = 4$$

> **Are the ordered pairs (3, 12) and (2, 8) in a proportional relationship? Explain.**

The ordered pairs (3, 12) and (2, 8) are / are not in a proportional relationship because _____

_____

_____

_____

_____

_____

SCORE ⓪ ① ②

0 = Incorrect or No Response
1 = Partial Response
2 = Complete and Accurate

BLOCK 5

Missing Numbers

> Use the graph to fill in the missing numbers in the story.

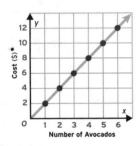

- Asim bought 4 avocados with a $20 bill.

- Asim's change was $_____.

- He bought _____ more avocados.

- Asim has $2 left.

> **How did you find the missing numbers?**

To find the first number, _____

_____

_____

To find the second number,

_____

_____

_____

Build It

> Use the numbers to create two equations that have the same proportional relationship. Use the $y = k \cdot x$ form. You may use one tile twice.

| 0.5 | 1 | 2 | 4 | 8 |

$$y = k \cdot x$$

_____ = _____ • _____

_____ = _____ • _____

> **How do you know that two linear equations have the same proportional relationship?**

I know that two linear equations have the same proportional relationshp when _____

_____

_____

_____

Who's Right?

> The ordered pair (3, 7) satisfies the equation $y = 2.5x$.

Cassie	Jose
False	True

Who's right? _____

> **Who is correct? How do you know?**

I know that _____ is correct because _____

_____

_____

_____

_____

LESSON 4

Brain Arcade

> Circle the sushi plates to create a product of 40.

_____ × _____ × _____ = 40

> Use the remaining numbers to create equations where the products are 24 and 25.

_____ = 24

_____ = 25

LESSON 5

Which Does Not Belong?

> Circle the ordered pair that does not belong.

| (3, 9) | (9, 27) | (8, 24) |

| (125, 375) | (4, 16) |

> What is another ordered pair that could also belong with this set? How do you know?

The ordered pair _____ could also belong with this set because

_____

_____

_____

_____

> In this Topic, you learned how to find solutions to a linear equation.

How do you know if an ordered pair is a solution to an equation?

Substitute the *x*- and the *y*-values from the ordered pair into the equation. If the coordinates satisfy the equation, it is a solution.

LESSON 1
PROBLEM SOLVING

Determine the Similarity of Right Triangles

> WORKED EXAMPLE

> TRY IT

> GUIDED LEARNING

1

2

Read It! Read the problem.

ARCHITECT

Nico's design uses triangular shapes. Triangle A is shown on the graph. Triangle B has the coordinates (0, 0), (3, 0), and (3, 4). Are Nico's triangles similar?

Triangle	Short Leg	Long Leg
A	1	2
B	3	4

Show It! Represent the problem.

Solve It! Solve the problem.

Short leg: 1•3 = 3

Long leg: 2•2 = 4

Nico's triangles are / are not similar.

Check It! Check your work.

Read It! Read the problem.

GRAPHIC DESIGNER

Maya needs to scale up a logo in the shape of a triangle for an ad. Are Maya's triangles in a proportional relationship?

Show It! Represent the problem.

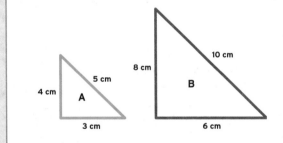

Solve It! Solve the problem.

Maya's triangles are / are not in a proportional relationship.

Check It! Check your work.

Read It! Read the problem.

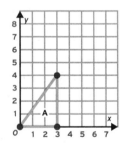

COSTUME DESIGNER

Luisa designs triangle patterns for costumes. Triangle A is shown on the graph. Triangle B has the coordinates (0, 0), (6, 0), and (6, 8). Are Luisa's triangles similar?

Triangle	Short Leg	Long Leg
A		
B		

Show It! Represent the problem.

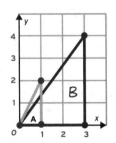

Solve It! Solve the problem.

Luisa's triangles are / are not similar.

Check It! Check your work.

PRACTICE

3

COMIC BOOK ARTIST

Ramon is drawing triangular shapes. Triangle A is shown on the graph. Triangle B has the coordinates (0, 0), (3, 0), and (3, 12). Are Ramon's triangles similar?

Triangle	Short Leg	Long Leg
A		
B		

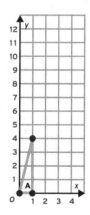

Ramon's triangles are / are not similar.

4

ANIMATOR

Arita is illustrating triangle shapes. Triangle A is shown on the graph. Triangle B has the coordinates (0, 0), (6, 0), and (6, 12). Are Arita's triangles similar?

Triangle	Short Leg	Long Leg
A		
B		

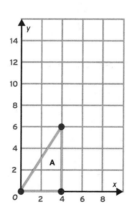

Arita's triangles are / are not similar.

Select all that apply.

Hachiro created four triangular pendants in different sizes.

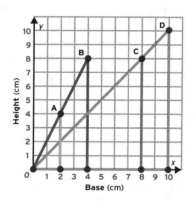

☐ Pendants A and B are similar.

☐ Pendants B and C are similar.

☐ Pendants C and D are similar.

☐ All the pendants are similar.

☐ None of the pendants are similar.

SCORE ⓪ ① ②

0 = Incorrect or No Response
1 = Partial Response
2 = Complete and Accurate

Interpret Points on a Graph as Solutions

> WORKED EXAMPLE

> TRY IT

> GUIDED LEARNING

The equation $y = 4x$ represents the time it takes a cartoon to move a certain distance. Are the points A (3, 16), B (7, 28), and C (8, 24) solutions to the equation?

STEP 1 Determine if point A represents a solution.

A (3, 16): $y = 4x$

$16 = 4 \cdot 3$

$16 \neq 12$

Is (3, 16) a solution? __no__

STEP 2 Determine if point B represents a solution.

B (7, 28): $y = 4x$

$28 = 4 \cdot 7$

$28 = 28$

Is (7, 28) a solution? __yes__

STEP 3 Determine if point C represents a solution.

C (8, 24): $y = 4x$

$24 = 4 \cdot 8$

$24 \neq 32$

Is (8, 24) a solution? __no__

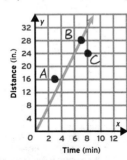

1

The equation $y = 1.5 \cdot x$ represents the time an artist spends priming canvases each day. Use the graph to determine if the points A (2, 3) and B (7, 12) satisfy the equation.

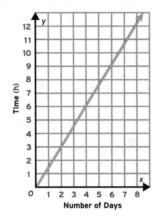

Does point A satisfy the equation $y = 1.5 \cdot x$? _____

Does point B satisfy the equation $y = 1.5 \cdot x$? _____

2

The equation $y = 3.5x$ represents the relationship between an image's height and width. Are the points A (2, 7), B (3, 8), and C (5, 17.5) solutions to the equation?

STEP 1 Determine if point A represents a solution.

A (2, 7): $y = 3.5x$

Is (2, 7) a solution? _____

STEP 2 Determine if point B represents a solution.

B (3, 8): $y = 3.5x$

Is (3, 8) a solution? _____

STEP 3 Determine if point C represents a solution.

C (5, 17.5): $y = 3.5x$

Is (5, 17.5) a solution? _____

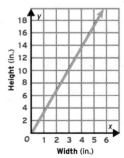

> PRACTICE

3

An artist sketches people quickly as they walk by on the street. The equation $y = 15x$ represents the relationship between the time and the number of sketches. Are the points A (1.5, 30), B (2, 40), and C (3, 45) solutions to the equation?

A (1.5, 30): $y = 15x$

Is (1.5, 30) a solution? _____

B (2, 40): $y = 15x$

Is (2, 40) a solution? _____

C (3, 45): $y = 15x$

Is (3, 45) a solution? _____

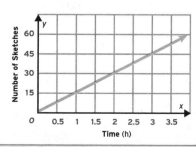

4

A printing machine can print 5 lines of text per second. The equation $y = 0.2x$ represents the relationship between the number of lines of text and time in seconds. Are the points A (3, 0.6), B (6, 1.2), and C (9, 1.6) solutions to the equation?

A (3, 0.6): $y = 0.2x$

Is (3, 0.6) a solution? _____

B (6, 1.2): $y = 0.2x$

Is (6, 1.2) a solution? _____

C (9, 1.6): $y = 0.2x$

Is (9, 1.6) a solution? _____

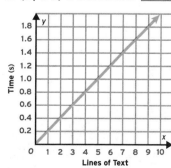

> **Solve the problem.**

An art teacher uses the equation $y = 3x$ to represent the relationship between the area of a painting and the time it takes to dry. Are the points A (1.5, 4.5) and B (2, 6.5) solutions to the equation?

A (1.5, 4.5): $y = 3x$

Is (1.5, 4.5) a solution? _____

B (2, 6.5): $y = 3x$

Is (2, 6.5) a solution? _____

> **If you were to graph this linear equation, which point would be on the line? How do you know?**

The point that would be on the line is _____

_____

_____

_____

_____

_____

TOPIC 3

TOPIC 2

TOPIC 1

SCORE ⓪ ① ②

0 = Incorrect or No Response
1 = Partial Response
2 = Complete and Accurate

LESSON 3
CONCEPT

Generate Solutions to Equations

> WORKED EXAMPLE

> TRY IT

> GUIDED LEARNING

WORKED EXAMPLE

A potter uses the equation $y = 25x$ to represent the relationship between the temperature of the kiln and the time it takes to heat up. What are some ordered pairs that are solutions to the equation?

STEP 1 Substitute to find a solution to the equation.

When $x = 10$: $y = 25x$
$y = 25 \cdot 10$
$y = 250$

STEP 2 Complete the table.

Time (min) x	Temperature (°C) y
0	0
10	250
20	500

STEP 3 Plot the ordered pairs on the graph.

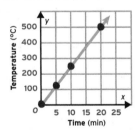

STEP 4 Find another ordered pair that solves the equation.

When $x = 5$: $y = 25x$
$y = 25 \cdot 5$
$y = 125$
Another solution: (5 , 125)

TRY IT

1 The equation $y = 3x$ represents the relationship between yards of fabric and the number of cushions that Alan can make. How many yards of fabric does Alan need to make 4 cushions?

Number of Cushions x	Length (yd) y
0	0
1	3
4	
6	18

Alan needs ____ yards of fabric to make 4 cushions.

GUIDED LEARNING

2 A graphic designer uses the equation $y = 0.5x$ to represent the relationship between the height and width of photos to recreate them on magazine pages. What are some ordered pairs that are solutions to the equation?

STEP 1 Substitute to find a solution to the equation.

When $x = 1$: $y = 0.5x$

STEP 2 Complete the table.

Height (in.) x	Width (in.) y
0	
1	
3	

STEP 3 Plot the ordered pairs on the graph.

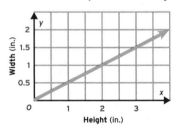

STEP 4 Find another ordered pair that solves the equation.

When $x = 2.5$: $y = 0.5x$

Another solution: (____ , ____)

ordered pair *(n)* a pair of numbers used to locate the position of a point on a coordinate plane

solution *(n)* an ordered pair that makes an equation true

> PRACTICE

3

A sculptor uses the equation $y = 1.5x$ to represent the relationship between cans of plaster and the number of figurines she can make. What are some ordered pairs that are solutions to the equation?

When $x = 1$: $y = 1.5x$

Number of Figurines x	Cans of Plaster y
1	
2	
3	

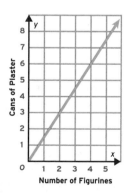

Number of Figurines

When $x = 5$: $y = 1.5x$

Another solution: (_____, _____)

4

Mikel, an illustrator for children's books, uses the equation $y = 1.25x$ to represent the relationship between time in hours and the number of pages he can illustrate. What are some ordered pairs that are solutions to the equation?

When $x = 1$: $y = 1.25x$

Time (h) x	Number of Pages y
1	
2	
4	

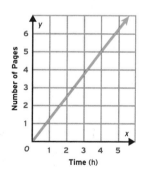

Time (h)

When $x = 3$: $y = 1.25x$

Another solution: (_____, _____)

EXIT Ticket

BLOCK 5 • TOPIC 3 • TOPIC 2 • TOPIC 1

> **Find and fix the errors.**

The equation $y = 4x$ represents the relationship between pints of paint and the area it can cover. What are some ordered pairs that are solutions to the equation?

Paint (pt) x	Area (sq m) y
1	4
2.5	10
3	0.75

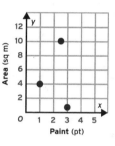

Paint (pt)

When $x = 3$: $y = 4x$

$$3 = 4 \cdot x$$

$$0.75 = x$$

Solution: (_3_, _0.75_)

I can use the graph to verify that I found the correct solutions by drawing a straight line through all the plotted points.

SCORE ⓪ ① ②
0 = Incorrect or No Response
1 = Partial Response
2 = Complete and Accurate

Solution Sets **25**

Reason With Proportional Relationships

I'll think carefully about which number should be the k-value in order to plot points that are solutions.

RULES

What's My Point? *(Level 2)*

What You Need
- *mSpace* pages 26–29
- Paper clips
- Pencils

What to Know
- One player is X and the other is O.
- Players may spin again if paper clip stops on the line.

How to Win
- The player to plot the most solutions to the graphed equations after 8 turns wins.

› **HOW TO PLAY**

STEP 1 Spin the spinner twice. Decide which will be the *x*-value and the *k*-value.

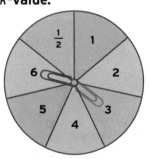

TURN	x	k	y = kx	(x, y)	SOLUTION?
1	6	3			
2					

STEP 2 Substitute the values into the equation, and evaluate to find *y*.

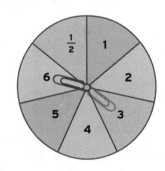

TURN	x	k	y = kx	(x, y)	SOLUTION?
1	6	3	y = 3•6		
2					

STEP 3 Record and plot the ordered pair.

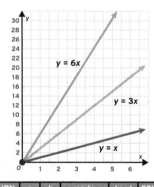

TURN	x	k	y = kx	(x, y)	SOLUTION?
1	6	3	y = 3•6	(6, 18)	
2					

STEP 4 Determine if the ordered pair is a solution to one of the graphed lines.

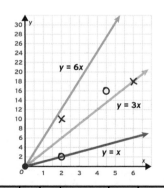

TURN	x	k	y = kx	(x, y)	SOLUTION?
1	6	3	y = 3•6	(6, 18)	yes
2					

RECORDING SHEET

What's My Point?
(Level 2)

> Record the equations and ordered pairs in the tables, and plot points on the graph.

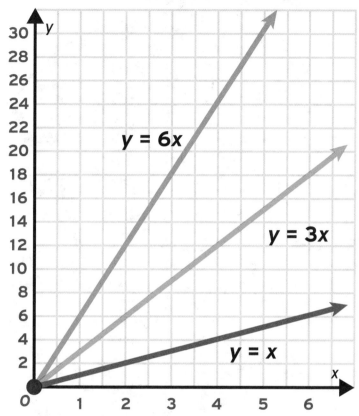

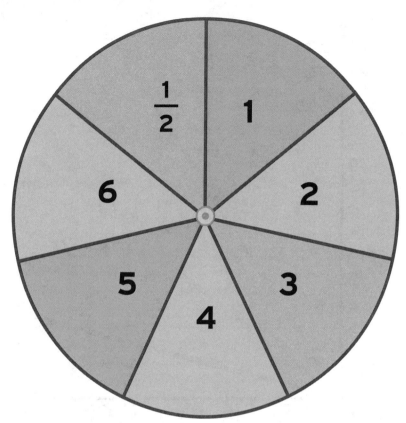

TURN	x	k	y = kx	(x, y)	SOLUTION?
1					
2					
3					
4					
5					
6					
7					
8					

TURN	x	k	y = kx	(x, y)	SOLUTION?
1					
2					
3					
4					
5					
6					
7					
8					

BLOCK 5 › TOPIC 2
LESSON 4
GAME

RECORDING SHEET
What's My Point?
(Level 2)

› Record the equations and ordered pairs in the tables, and plot points on the graph.

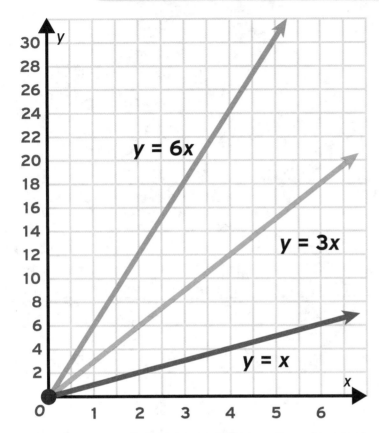

TURN	x	k	y = kx	(x, y)	SOLUTION?
1					
2					
3					
4					
5					
6					
7					
8					

TURN	x	k	y = kx	(x, y)	SOLUTION?
1					
2					
3					
4					
5					
6					
7					
8					

COMIC BOOK ARTISTS illustrate comic books by drawing characters and scenes to scale. When creating sketches from a photograph, they make the dimensions proportional when shrinking or enlarging the size of the drawing.

The image below is a sketch of the Sushi Monster.

> Use the grid lines to make a sketch of the Sushi Monster that is 2 times as large.

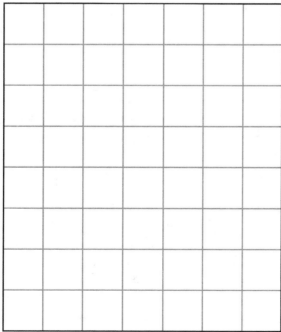

EXIT Ticket

BLOCK 5

TOPIC 3

> **Answer this question.**

Are the points (6, 3), (8, 16), and (10, 5) collinear? Explain.

(6, 3): $y = kx$ $k =$ _____

(8, 16): $y = kx$ $k =$ _____

TOPIC 2

(10, 5): $y = kx$ $k =$ _____

The solutions (6, 3), (8, 16), and (10, 5) are / are not collinear because _____

TOPIC 1

_____

_____

_____

_____

SCORE ⓪ ① ②   **0** = Incorrect or No Response
1 = Partial Response
2 = Complete and Accurate

Reason About Solution Sets

> WORKED EXAMPLE

> TRY IT

> GUIDED LEARNING

Kayla needs new sketchbooks. Each book costs $16. The equation $y = 16x$ represents the relationship between the number of sketchbooks and the cost. Kayla has $76 to spend. How many sketchbooks can she buy?

STEP 1 Identify the variables.

x represents the <u>number of books</u>.

y represents the <u>total cost.</u>

$k =$ <u>16</u>

STEP 2 Find the value of x.

$$y = kx$$
$$76 = 16x$$
$$\frac{76}{16} = \frac{16x}{16}$$
$$4.75 = x \text{ or } x = 4.75$$

Solution: (<u>4.75</u>, <u>76</u>)

STEP 3 Reason about the value of x.

The solution does/(does not) make sense in this situation because

<u>Kayla cannot buy part of a</u>

<u>sketchbook.</u>

STEP 4 Solve the problem.

Kayla can buy <u>4</u> sketchbooks with $76.

1

A photographer sells his photos of New York City for $22 each. The equation $y = 22x$ represents the relationship between the price and the number of photos. Jayden has $50. How many photos can Jayden buy?

Jayden can buy _____ photos with $50.

Will he use all his money? _____

2

Ethan, a glass worker, can make 1 vase in 0.8 hours. The equation $y = 0.8x$ represents the relationship between the number of vases and the time. Ethan can work for only 7 hours today. How many vases can he make?

STEP 1 Identify the variables.

x represents the _____

y represents the _____

$k =$ _____

STEP 2 Find the value of x.

$$y = kx$$

Solution: (_____, _____)

STEP 3 Reason about the value of x.

The solution does/does not make sense in this situation because

_____

_____

STEP 4 Solve the problem.

Ethan can make _____ vases in 7 hours.

> PRACTICE

3 Hans, a clothing designer, has $38 to buy zippers. Each zipper costs $2.50. The equation $y = 2.50x$ represents the relationship between the number of zippers and the cost. How many zippers can Hans buy?

x represents the _____

y represents the _____

$k =$ _____

$$y = kx$$

Solution: (_____, _____)

The solution does / does not make sense in this situation because

_____

_____

Hans can buy _____ zippers.

4 Lin, an illustrator, pays $40 for each art class she attends. The equation $y = 40x$ represents the relationship between the number of classes and the amount Lin spends. She has $550 to spend. How many art classes can Lin pay for?

x represents the _____

y represents the _____

$k =$ _____

$$y = kx$$

Solution: (_____, _____)

The solution does / does not make sense in this situation because

_____

_____

Lin can pay for _____ art classes.

EXIT Ticket

BLOCK **5**

TOPIC 3

> **Solve the problem.**

Marty has $50 to spend at a comic book festival. Each comic book costs $8. The equation $y = 8x$ represents the relationship between the number of comic books and the cost. How many comic books can Marty buy?

x represents the _____

y represents the _____

Marty can buy _____ comic books.

> **How much money will Marty have left over after buying 6 comic books? Explain.**

Marty will have $_____ left over after buying comic books because _____

_____

_____

_____

TOPIC 2

TOPIC 1

BLOCK 5

LESSON 1

Brain Teaser

> **Find the total lengths of the shortest and longest paths from points A to D. The length of each diagonal path is 5 feet.**

Your paths must:

- Visit each point at least once
- Not retrace any lines
- Never leave the figure

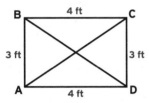

The ratio of the length of the shortest to the longest path is

_____.

> **How did you find the paths?**

To find the shortest path, _____

_____

_____

To find the longest path, _____

_____

_____

_____

LESSON 2

Build It

> **Use the numbers to complete the four equations. You may use numbers more than once.**

| 2.5 | 7 | 15 | 17.5 | 32.5 | 105 |

_____ + _____ = _____

_____ − _____ = _____

_____ · _____ = _____

_____ ÷ _____ = _____

> **Why can you write a multiplication equation with the same numbers two different ways?**

You can write a multiplication equation with the same numbers two different ways because

_____

_____

_____

LESSON 3

Make an Estimate

> **Choose the best estimate from the list for the percent of water in each glass.**

| 10% | 25% | 50% | 75% | 90% | 100% |

> **How can the percent of water in each glass be different if the height of the water is the same?**

The percent of water in each glass can be different because _____

_____

_____

_____

_____

LESSON 4

Number Strings

> Work backwards to fill in the missing numbers.

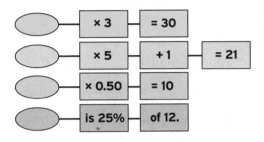

⬭	× 3	= 30
⬭	× 5	+ 1
⬭	× 0.50	= 10
⬭	is 25%	of 12.

(× 5 and + 1 lead to = 21)

> How did you begin to fill in the missing numbers?

I began by _____

_____

_____

_____

_____

_____

LESSON 5

Who's Right?

> The equation $y = 0.75x$ represents the relationship between student and adult ticket prices at a show.

x represents the adult ticket price. The adult ticket price is greater.	y represents the student ticket price. The student ticket price is greater.

Who's right? _____

> Write True or False for each of the statements for the values of the variables in the form $y = kx$.

- _____ If k is greater than 1, then y is greater than x.

- _____ If k is greater than 1, then y is less than x.

- _____ If k is between 0 and 1, then y is less than x.

> In this Topic, you learned how to use a percent as the constant of proportionality in a proportional equation.

How can I represent the statement "y is 25% of x" in an equation?

I know that x and y have a proportional relationship. So I can represent this using the equation $y = 0.25x$.

Solve Ratio Problems Using Equations

> WORKED EXAMPLE

Zoe creates a print of a painting using a ratio of painting measurements to print measurements of 5:1. The painting has a width of 0.5 meter. Find the width of the print.

STEP 1 Analyze the problem.

x represents the _painting measurements._

y represents the _print measurements._

STEP 2 Solve for the constant of proportionality, k.

$$y = kx$$
$$1 = k \cdot 5$$
$$\frac{1}{5} = \frac{k \cdot 5}{5}$$
$$0.2 = k \text{ or } k = 0.2$$

STEP 3 Express the relationship with an equation, $y = kx$.

Equation: _y = 0.2x_

STEP 4 Solve the problem.

$$y = 0.2x$$
$$y = 0.2 \cdot 0.5$$
$$y = 0.1$$

The width of the print is _0.1_ meter.

> TRY IT

1

Kai is building a house using a ratio of blueprint dimensions to actual dimensions of 1:50. Write an equation so Kai can use the blueprint dimensions to find the actual dimensions.

x represents the blueprint dimensions.

y represents the actual dimensions.

Equation: _____

> GUIDED LEARNING

2

Jade builds a scale model of a bridge. She uses a ratio of model measurements to bridge measurements of 5:20. The beams in the model are 2.5 feet long. Find the length of the beams on the actual bridge.

STEP 1 Analyze the problem.

x represents the _____

_____

y represents the _____

_____

STEP 2 Solve for the constant of proportionality, k.

STEP 3 Express the relationship with an equation, $y = kx$.

Equation: _____

STEP 4 Solve the problem.

The length of the beams on the actual bridge is _____ feet.

> PRACTICE

3

Kim projects an image using a ratio of image measurements to projection measurements of 2:9. A car in the image has a width of 0.2 meter. Find the width of the car in the projection.

x represents the _____

_____

y represents the _____

_____

Equation: _____

The width of the car in the projection is _____ meter.

4

Dante builds a scale model of a house with a ratio of actual measurements to model measurements of 4:3. The length of the porch is 18 meters. Find the length of the porch in the model.

x represents the _____

_____

y represents the _____

_____

Equation: _____

The length of the porch in the model is _____ meters.

EXIT Ticket

BLOCK **5**

TOPIC 3

> *Select all that apply.*

A photo with a height of 10 inches is enlarged to make a poster with a height of 30 inches.

☐ A car with a height of 2 inches in the photo has a height of 6 inches in the poster.

☐ A car with a height of 8 inches in the poster has a height of 3 inches in the photo.

TOPIC 2

☐ A tree with a height of 24 inches in the poster has a height of 8 inches in the photo.

☐ A tree with a height of 6 inches in the photo has a height of 18 inches in the poster.

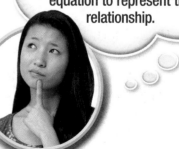

If I know the ratio that relates two quantities, I can write a $y = kx$ equation to represent the relationship.

TOPIC 1

SCORE ⓪ ① ②

0 = Incorrect or No Response
1 = Partial Response
2 = Complete and Accurate

Applications of Percent **35**

Model Proportional Relationships

> WORKED EXAMPLE

Rafi, a sports photographer, takes action photos of hockey players. Based on the graph, how many seconds will Rafi need to take 1500 photos?

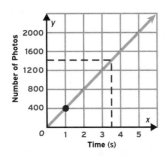

STEP 1 **Make an estimate.**

Estimate: between 3 and 4 seconds

STEP 2 **Identify the constant of proportionality, *k*.**

Unit rate: 400 photos per second

$k = 400$

STEP 3 **Write an equation.**

Equation: $y = 400x$

$1500 = 400x$

STEP 4 **Solve the problem.**

$$\frac{1500}{400} = \frac{400x}{400}$$

$3.75 = x$ or $x = 3.75$

Rafi will need 3.75 seconds to take 1500 photos.

> TRY IT

1 The equation $y = 8x$ represents the relationship between the amount of time Shanay takes to weave thread into fabric and the number of rows. How long will it take Shanay to weave 72 rows of fabric at this constant rate?

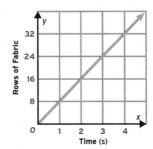

It will take Shanay _____ seconds to weave 72 rows of fabric.

> GUIDED LEARNING

2 Chris, an architect, uses a laser cutter to make a stainless-steel model. Based on the graph, how long does the laser cutter take to cut stainless steel that is 108 cm thick?

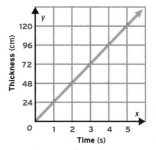

STEP 1 **Make an estimate.**

Estimate: _____

STEP 2 **Identify the constant of proportionality, *k*.**

Unit rate: _____

$k =$ _____

STEP 3 **Write an equation.**

Equation:

STEP 4 **Solve the problem.**

The laser cutter takes _____ seconds to cut through stainless steel that is 108 cm thick.

> PRACTICE

3 To create a movie, film reels with frames of images run through a projector. Based on the graph, what length of film reel can fit 100 frames?

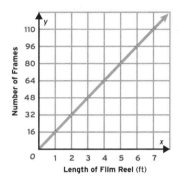

Number of Frames vs. Length of Film Reel (ft)

Estimate: _____

Unit rate: _____

k = _____

Equation:

_____ feet of film reel can fit 100 frames.

4 Lindsi, a film editor, edits films for errors and cuts out unnecessary scenes. Based on the graph, how long will it take Lindsi to edit 6.3 minutes of film?

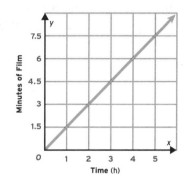

Minutes of Film vs. Time (h)

Estimate: _____

Unit rate: _____

_____

k = _____

Equation:

It will take Lindsi _____ hours to edit 6.3 minutes of film.

> **Solve the problem.**

An urban designer uses a computer program to simulate sketches of a park at different times of the day. Based on the graph, how long will the program take to simulate 16 sketches?

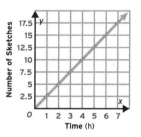

Number of Sketches vs. Time (h)

The program will take _____ hours to simulate 16 sketches.

> **Explain how you cannot use this graph to find the exact answer.**

I cannot use this graph to find an exact answer because _____

_____

_____

_____

_____

SCORE ⓪ ① ②   0 = Incorrect or No Response
1 = Partial Response
2 = Complete and Accurate

TOPIC 3

TOPIC 2

TOPIC 1

Find the Part Using Equations

BLOCK 5

> WORKED EXAMPLE

Lily, an art dealer, earns 45% of a painting's price. Lily sells a painting for $500. How much money does Lily earn from selling this painting?

STEP 1 Identify the variables.

y is __45__ % of x.

x represents the _painting's price._

y represents the _earnings._

STEP 2 Express the percent as a decimal.

Decimal: $45\% = \frac{45}{100}$

$= 0.45$

STEP 3 Write an equation.

Equation: $y = kx$

$y = 0.45x$

$y = 0.45 \cdot 500$

STEP 4 Solve the problem.

$y = $ __225__

Lily earns $ __225__ from selling this painting.

> TRY IT

1 A furniture designer constructs a model of a chair that is 15% of the chair's actual size. The height of the actual chair is 40 inches. The relationship between the heights of the actual chair and the model chair can be expressed as $y = 0.15x$. What is the height of the model chair?

The height of the model chair is _____ inches.

> GUIDED LEARNING

2 Movies are filmed with wide-screen images. A movie in full screen is only 65% of the wide-screen image. A wide-screen image is 720 pixels long. How many pixels long is the image in full screen?

STEP 1 Identify the variables.

y is _____ % of x.

x represents the _____

_____

y represents the _____

_____

STEP 2 Express the percent as a decimal.

Decimal:

STEP 3 Write an equation.

Equation: $y = kx$

STEP 4 Solve the problem.

$y = $ _____

The image in full screen is _____ pixels long.

> **PRACTICE**

3

A photographer crops a photo to reframe the subject. The original photo has a length of 18 inches. The length of the new photo is 47% of the original photo's length. What is the length of the new photo?

STEP 1 **Identify the variables.**

y is _____% of *x*.

x represents the _____

_____

y represents the _____

_____

STEP 2 **Express the percent as a decimal.**

Decimal:

STEP 3 **Write an equation.**

$y = \underline{}x$

STEP 4 **Solve the problem.**

$y = \underline{}$

The length of the new photo is _____ inches.

4

A science museum curator orders a model of a dinosaur bone for a display. The actual bone is 7 inches thick. The model bone is 70% of the thickness of the actual bone. How thick is the model bone?

STEP 1 **Identify the variables.**

y is _____% of *x*.

x represents the _____

_____

y represents the _____

_____

STEP 2 **Express the percent as a decimal.**

Decimal:

STEP 3 **Write an equation.**

$y = \underline{}x$

STEP 4 **Solve the problem.**

$y = \underline{}$

The model bone is _____ inches thick.

EXIT Ticket

BLOCK **5**

> **Solve the problem.**

A landscape architect is redesigning a garden. The area of the new garden is 83% of the area of the original garden. The original garden had an area of 800 square feet. What is the area of the new garden?

The area of the new garden is _____ square feet.

When I find a percent of a number, I express the percent as a decimal. Then I can use it as the constant of proportionality in the equation $y = kx$.

TOPIC 3

TOPIC 2

TOPIC 1

SCORE ⓪ ① ②

0 = Incorrect or No Response
1 = Partial Response
2 = Complete and Accurate

Solve Percent Problems Using Equations

> **WORKED EXAMPLE**

Shaquan, an art gallery owner, received 78% of the monthly gallery budget from private donations. The gallery budget this month is $5000. How much money does Shaquan receive from private donations this month?

STEP 1 Identify the variables.

y is __78__ % of x.

x represents the _amount of the monthly gallery budget._

y represents the _amount from private donations._

STEP 2 Express the percent as a decimal.

Decimal: $78\% = \frac{78}{100}$

$= 0.78$

STEP 3 Write an equation.

Equation: $y = kx$

$y = 0.78x$

$y = 0.78 \cdot 5000$

STEP 4 Solve the problem.

$y = 3900$

Shaquan received $ __3900__ from private donations this month.

> **TRY IT**

1

Finley, a playwright, has written 2 scenes of his play. This is 25% of his whole play. How many scenes will there be in Finley's play when it is complete?

2 is 25% of _____.

There will be _____ scenes in Finley's play when it is complete.

> **GUIDED LEARNING**

2

Auguste Rodin, a sculptor, made a statue called "The Thinker," which sits on a base. The statue weighs 2100 pounds alone. This is 15% of the total weight. How much do the statue and base weigh altogether?

STEP 1 Identify the variables.

y is _____% of x.

x represents the _____

_____

y represents the _____

_____

STEP 2 Express the percent as a decimal.

Decimal:

STEP 3 Write an equation.

Equation: $y = kx$

STEP 4 Solve the problem.

The statue and base weigh _____ pounds altogether.

> PRACTICE

3

A film editor cuts unwanted scenes from a film. The running time of the edited film is 111 minutes. This is 60% of the running time of the original film. How long was the running time of the original film?

STEP 1 **Identify the variables.**

y is _____% of x.

x represents the _____

_____

y represents the _____

_____

STEP 2 **Express the percent as a decimal.**

Decimal:

STEP 3 **Write an equation.**

Equation: y = _____ • x

STEP 4 **Solve the problem.**

The running time of the original film was _____ minutes.

4

Dee, a makeup artist for a movie, needs to work on a total of 50 actors. Dee has worked on 8% of the actors. How many actors has Dee worked on so far?

STEP 1 **Identify the variables.**

y is _____% of x.

x represents the _____

_____

y represents the _____

_____

STEP 2 **Express the percent as a decimal.**

Decimal:

STEP 3 **Write an equation.**

Equation: y = _____ • x

STEP 4 **Solve the problem.**

Dee has worked on _____ actors so far.

EXIT Ticket

BLOCK 5

> **Solve the problem.**

An artist is making a print of her sketch. The area of the print is 60% of the area of her sketch. The print has an area of 90 square inches. What is the area of her sketch?

The area of her sketch is _____ square inches.

> **Is the area of the print or her sketch greater? How do you know this without doing any calculations?**

The area of the _____ is greater than the area of the print because _____

_____

_____

TOPIC 3

TOPIC 2

TOPIC 1

SCORE ⓪ ① ②   **0** = Incorrect or No Response
1 = Partial Response
2 = Complete and Accurate

LESSON 5
PROBLEM SOLVING

ANCHOR VIDEO CONNECTION

As the Anchor Video shows, you can compare proportional relationships that are represented in graphs and equations.

> EXPLORE

Use Models to Compare Options

> **You are an up-and-coming artist. You have apprenticeship offers from two mentor artists, Sara and Ravi.**

As an apprentice, you will receive a commission for any of your mentor's pieces of art that you sell. Your task is to evaluate the two offers and determine whether you should work as an apprentice for Sara or Ravi.

Commission Details

- Sara's pieces of art sell for $25 each. Your commission is 60%.
- Ravi's pieces of art sell for $2000 each. Your commission is 25%.

A CREATE

For each mentor artist, write an equation and graph a line showing the proportional relationship between the pieces of art sold and your total commission.

Sara's Offer

x represents the number of pieces of art sold.

y represents the total commission.

k represents the commission per piece of art.

$k =$

Equation: _____

Commission ($)

Number of Pieces of Art

Ravi's Offer

x represents the number of pieces of art sold.

y represents the total commission.

k represents the commission per piece of art.

$k =$

Equation: _____

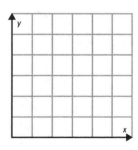

Commission ($)

Number of Pieces of Art

BIG IDEA 1 Proportional relationships can be represented with tables, graphs, and equations.

BIG IDEA 2 Modeling a situation with an equation helps us to find a solution for any value.

B PREDICT

The current ratio of Sara's sales to Ravi's sales is 100:2. Would you earn a greater total commission with Sara or Ravi?

_____

_____

_____

_____

_____

_____

_____

C EXPLAIN

As a professional artist, assume you will make pieces of art that sell at the same sales ratio as the artist with whom you apprenticed. Would you earn more as a professional after apprenticing for Sara or Ravi?

_____

_____

_____

_____

_____

_____

EXIT Ticket

BLOCK 5

TOPIC 3

> **Solve the problem.**

The value of Sara's art increases to $40 per piece of art. How much money will you earn for every 100 pieces of art you sell as a professional artist if you had apprenticed for Sara?

TOPIC 2

I would earn $_____ for every 100 pieces of art I sell.

> **Does this change your decision? Explain your reasoning.**

TOPIC 1

_____

_____

_____

_____

SCORE ⓪ ① ②

| 0 = Incorrect or No Response |
| 1 = Partial Response |
| 2 = Complete and Accurate |

> YOUR JOB
Muralist

> YOUR TASK
Create a mural to scale
of New York City's tallest
skyscrapers.

ANCHOR VIDEO
CONNECTION

As the Anchor Video shows,
equations are useful for
reducing actual sizes when
creating scale models.

Create a Scaled Mural

> You are creating a scaled mural of skyscrapers for an exhibit.
The mural will have a height of 5.5 meters. You must follow the
proportional relationships between the heights of the skyscrapers
in your mural.

A EXPLORE

The graph shows the actual heights of five skyscrapers in New York City.
The heights include the spires. Use the information in the graph to find the
proportional relationship of the tallest building—One World Trade Center—
to its image in the mural. Complete the table. Then, write an equation to
represent the relationship between the actual heights and the mural heights.

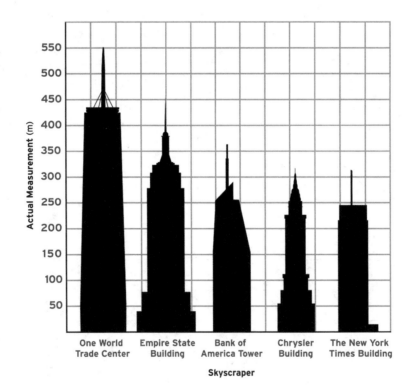

Height Ratios	
Actual Height (m)	Mural Height (m)
	5.5
110	
100	
10	
1	

$y = \underline{\quad\quad} x$

B APPLY

Use the equation you wrote to complete the table and graph.

Skyscraper	Actual Height x	Process y = _____ x	Mural Height y
One World Trade Center			
Empire State Building			
Bank of America Tower			
Chrysler Building			
The New York Times Building			

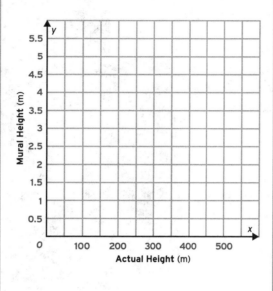

C ANALYZE

EXPLAIN How did you write the equation for the proportional relationship?

_____

_____

_____

_____

REFLECT Could you use the x = 100y equation to check your work in Apply? Why or why not?

_____

_____

_____

_____

Evaluate

> **Rate how well you and your partner understood and completed each part of the performance task.**

Ranking Scale			
None	Limited	Partial	Thorough
0	1	2	3

A Found the equation for the mural heights.

| Me | 0 | 1 | 2 | 3 |
| Partner | 0 | 1 | 2 | 3 |

B Accurately completed the table and graph for the mural heights.

| Me | 0 | 1 | 2 | 3 |
| Partner | 0 | 1 | 2 | 3 |

C Answered each question thoughtfully.

| Me | 0 | 1 | 2 | 3 |
| Partner | 0 | 1 | 2 | 3 |

EXTEND

How could you compare the actual heights to mural heights of the skyscrapers to check your work?

_____

_____

_____

_____

_____

BLOCK 5

MINDSET STRATEGY

Reflect on Expanding Mental Capacity

Congratulations! You've completed Block 5 of *MATH 180*.

Train Your Memory

What happens when you learn something? Scientists have been asking this question for decades. What they found is that learning physically changes your brain. **Your brain actually grows.**

Studying Cab Drivers

How did they find this out? In one well-known study, psychologist Eleanor Maguire at University College London studied the brains of London cab drivers. The drivers had spent years learning over 25,000 jumbled streets in central London.

Looking Inside the Brain

Maguire and her team used MRI technology to look inside the cab drivers' brains. The part of their brain responsible for spatial reasoning, located in the hippocampus (shown on right), had grown over time. It turns out learning something new actually makes your brain grow!

> **Think back to the beginning of the year. What are two math skills you can do now that you couldn't do before?**

1. _____

_____

2. _____

_____

> **How did you learn these skills?**

_____

_____

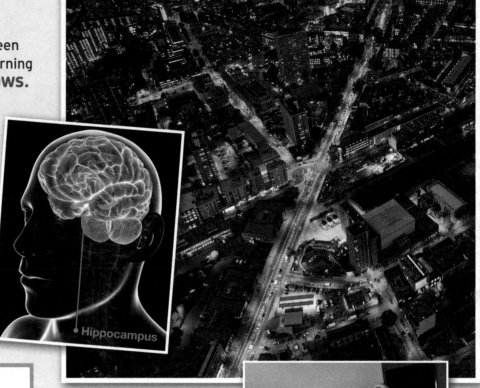

Hippocampus

London cab drivers must pass a difficult test where they must memorize over 300 standard routes through central London.

Magnetic Resource Imaging, or MRI, uses magnetic fields to generate 3-D images of different body parts, including the brain.

How to "Build Your Brain"

> When you practice and put in effort, your brain cells grow new connections that make you smarter!

1 Choose a challenge.
- ☑ Set a goal that's a little hard for you.
- ☑ Raise the challenge level as you learn.

2 Get in a growth mindset.
- ☑ Picture your brain cells growing.
- ☑ Remember that learning makes you smarter!

3 Get focused.
- ☑ Start now and make a plan.
- ☑ When it gets tough, stick with it.

4 Stay healthy.
- ☑ Sleep 9–10 hours a night.
- ☑ Exercise at least 3 times a week.

5 Practice.
- ☑ Find out what skills you need to achieve your goal.
- ☑ Practice them, and ask for help when you need it.

Putting It Into Practice

> Make a plan to use the strategies above to increase your math skills.

> First, choose one challenge in *MATH 180* and set a goal.

_____

_____

> Next, explain how you will reach your goal using two of the other strategies above.

VOCABULARY

- coefficient
- constant
- estimate
- initial value
- linear equation
- rate
- slope
- y-intercept

Good Money

How can small businesses solve big problems?

In this Anchor Video, see how some entrepreneurs use linear relationships to get their ideas off the ground.

Math in Business

In this Block, you will explore how math is used in entrepreneurship and business.

Financial Advisors

estimate the average person would need to invest about **$8000 per year** for **30 years** to be a millionaire.

Electricians

use **proportional relationships** to make electrical calculations when wiring a new building.

Restaurant Owners

have to keep prices affordable even when the costs of ingredients rise so they can stay in business. The menu price is usually about **4 times** the cost of ingredients.

Some

Retail Associates

earn a **fixed commission**, or fee, on every item sold in addition to their **hourly wages**.

A common pitfall for

Small Business Owners

is bad pricing. In clothing companies, owners have to account for all of the fabric when calculating **variable costs**, or costs that change, including the wasted fabric. The price of the product should be about **2.5 times** the cost of the materials.

BLOCK 6

LESSON 1

Block Preview

> **Look at the Career Explorations on _mSpace_ page 47. Which career interests you the most? Why?**

The career that interests me

most is _____

because _____

_____

> **Why is math important for running a business?**

Math is important for running a

business because _____

_____

_____

_____

_____

LESSON 2

Brain Teaser

> **Find the values of the items in the grocery bags.**

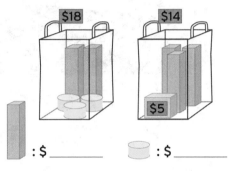

$18 $14

$5

⬚ : $ _____   ⬚ : $ _____

> **How did you begin working on this problem?**

I began working on this problem

by _____

_____

_____

_____

_____

LESSON 3

Find the Pattern

> **Find the rule that applies to the ordered pairs inside the circle.**

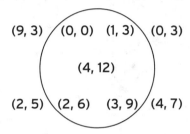

(9, 3) (0, 0) (1, 3) (0, 3)

(4, 12)

(2, 5) (2, 6) (3, 9) (4, 7)

The rule is _____.

> **How did you find the rule for the numbers inside the circle?**

I found the rule by _____

_____

_____

_____

_____

_____

LESSON 4

Tell Me All That You Can

> **About $y = 4x + 5$.**

- _____
- _____
- _____
- _____

> **What is a situation that can be represented by the equation?**

A situation that can be modeled by the equation is _____

_____

_____

_____

_____

_____

LESSON 5

Brain Arcade

> **Circle the bugs with sums less than 0.**

> **Find the sum of each expression circled.**

- _____ + _____ = _____
- _____ + _____ = _____
- _____ + _____ = _____
- _____ + _____ = _____

Sum It Up!

> **In this Topic, you learned how to write a linear equation from a graph, a table, and a description.**

What quantities do I need to find when writing a linear equation?

You need to find the rate and the initial value.

LESSON 1
PROBLEM SOLVING

ANCHOR VIDEO CONNECTION

As the Anchor Video shows, growing a business can increase its profits and total value.

BLOCK 6

Compare Business Plans With Equations

> **You want to expand your business to increase its total value. You need to evaluate your options.**

An investor will initially increase the value of your business, but will take a percent of your future profits.

A loan will initially decrease the value of your business, but 100% of future profits will belong to your business.

Business Options

Option 1: Find an Investor
• Initial value: + $60,000
• Annual growth: + $3000

Option 2: Take a Loan
• Initial value: − $60,000
• Annual growth: + $12,000

A CREATE

Complete the tables with the total values of your business for each option in both 5 years and 20 years.

Option 1: Investor		Option 2: Loan	
5 years	20 years	5 years	20 years

Total Value (Option 1)

Total Value (Option 2)

BIG IDEA 1 A linear relationship has a constant rate of change.

BIG IDEA 2 Representing linear relationships with tables, graphs, and equations helps us to find unknown values.

B PREDICT

Which option will increase the total value of your business more?

_____

_____

_____

_____

_____

_____

_____

C EXPLAIN

How is finding the value of the business the same for each option?
How is it different?

_____

_____

_____

_____

_____

_____

_____

EXIT Ticket

BLOCK 6

> **Find and fix the error.**

Aiden spends $100 on a lawnmower. He charges $15 for each lawn he mows. How much money does Aiden earn mowing 10 lawns?

$$\$100 \cdot 10 = \$1000$$

$$\$1000 - \$15 = \$985$$

Aiden has $ _985_ after mowing 10 lawns.

TOPIC 3

TOPIC 2

TOPIC 1

I can compare business plans by writing equations to find the total profits for any number of years and then adding or subtracting the initial value.

SCORE ⓪ ① ②

0 = Incorrect or No Response
1 = Partial Response
2 = Complete and Accurate

Write a Linear Equation From a Graph

> **WORKED EXAMPLE**

> **TRY IT**

> **GUIDED LEARNING**

Ted and Keisha rent kayaks. Keisha is 40 feet in front of Ted. They both start at the same time and travel 20 feet per minute. Express the distances traveled by Ted and Keisha with equations.

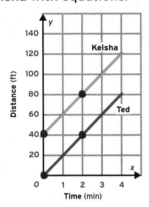

STEP 1 Find the values.

Ted:	Keisha:
(0, __0__)	(0, __40__)
(2, __40__)	(2, __80__)

STEP 2 Describe the patterns.

<u>Keisha</u> is always __40__ feet ahead of <u>Ted</u>.

STEP 3 Find the rate.

Rate: 20 feet per minute

STEP 4 Write the equations.

Ted: __y = 20x__

Keisha: __y = 20x + 40__

---

1 Shakira makes and sells necklaces. She has saved $40. She will earn $20 more each week. How much money will Shakira have in 3 weeks?

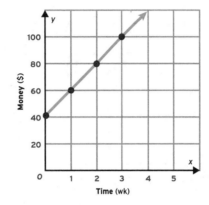

In 3 weeks, Shakira will have $_____.

---

2 Juliet and Mimi each start a food truck business. Mimi has $500 to start. They each draw up a business plan showing a profit of $250 per day. Express Juliet's and Mimi's earnings with equations.

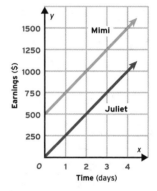

STEP 1 Find the values.

Juliet:	Mimi:
(0, _____)	(0, _____)
(3, _____)	(3, _____)

STEP 2 Describe the patterns.

_____ always has $_____ more than _____.

STEP 3 Find the rate.

Rate: $_____

STEP 4 Write the equations.

Juliet: _____

Mimi: _____

initial value *(n)* the starting or first value of a function; often the value of *y* when *x* = 0

equation *(n)* a mathematical sentence that states that two quantities or expressions are equal

> PRACTICE

3

Ayla and Mina are making phone cases at a tech fair. Mina has made 12 phone cases when Ayla arrives. They each make 3 phone cases per hour. Express the number of phone cases Ayla and Mina make as equations.

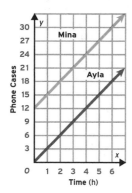

STEP 1 Find the values.

Ayla: Mina:

(0, _____)   (0, _____)

(3, _____)   (3, _____)

STEP 2 Describe the patterns.

_____ is always _____ phone cases ahead of _____.

STEP 3 Find the rate.

Rate: _____

STEP 4 Write the equations.

Ayla: _____

Mina: _____

4

Chen and Todd are delivering brochures for a job fair. Todd starts 25 miles ahead. Both their trucks travel 50 miles per hour. Express the distances traveled by Todd and Chen with equations.

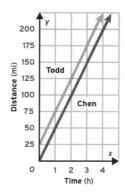

STEP 1 Find the values.

Chen: Todd:

(0, _____)   (0, _____)

(1, _____)   (1, _____)

STEP 2 Describe the patterns.

_____ is always _____ miles ahead of _____.

STEP 3 Find the rate.

Rate: _____

STEP 4 Write the equations.

Chen: _____

Todd: _____

> **Solve the problem.**

TOPIC 3

Jill, an interpreter, charges $50 per hour for sign language. She charges an extra $100 for voice translation. Express Jill's earnings with equations.

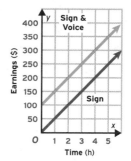

Sign:

(0, _____)

(4, _____)

Equation: _____

Sign & Voice:

(0, _____)

(4, _____)

Equation: _____

TOPIC 2

TOPIC 1

The initial value of a line tells me where the graph begins on the *y*-axis.

SCORE ⓪ ① ②

0 = Incorrect or No Response
1 = Partial Response
2 = Complete and Accurate

Write a Linear Equation From a Table

> WORKED EXAMPLE

> TRY IT

> GUIDED LEARNING

Tony and Maria are retail associates paid at the same hourly rate. Maria received a holiday bonus. Express Tony's and Maria's earnings with equations.

Time (h)	Earnings ($)	
	Tony	Maria
0	0	12
1	9	21
2	18	30
3	27	39

STEP 1 Find the rate.

Rate: $ _9 per hour_

STEP 2 Compare the values.

$$12 - 0 = 12$$
$$21 - 9 = 12$$
$$30 - 18 = 12$$
$$39 - 27 = 12$$

Maria always has $ _12_ more than _Tony_.

STEP 3 Write the equations.

Tony: _e = 9t_

Maria: _e = 9t + 12_

---

1 Tim and Luisa are testing a new two-person kayak for their rental business. Tim is sitting 3 feet in front of Luisa. What are Luisa's and Tim's distances at 5 seconds?

Time (s)	Distance (ft)	
	Luisa	Tim
0	0	3
1	2	5
2	4	7
3	6	9
5		

---

2 Ed and Inez are moving a new entertainment center on a hand truck into their furniture store. Express Ed's and Inez's distances with equations.

Time (min)	Distance (ft)	
	Ed	Inez
0	0	5
1	7	12
2	14	19
5	35	40

STEP 1 Find the rate.

Rate: _____

STEP 2 Compare the values.

_____ is always _____ feet ahead of _____.

STEP 3 Write the equations.

Ed: _____

Inez: _____

initial value *(n)* the starting or first value of a function; often the value of *y* when *x* = 0

rate *(n)* a comparison between two quantities with different units of measure

> PRACTICE

---

3 Ming and Zach both charge the same hourly rate to rent out their food trucks. Zach charges a cleaning fee. Express Ming's and Zach's charges with equations.

Time (h)	Charges ($)	
	Ming	Zach
0	0	45
1	24	69
3	72	117
5	120	165

STEP 1 Find the rate.

Rate: $_____

STEP 2 Compare the values.

_____ always charges $_____ more than _____.

STEP 3 Write the equations.

Ming: _____

Zach: _____

---

4 Paco, a waterskiing instructor, is towing Kate 90 feet behind his boat. Express Kate's and Paco's distances with equations.

Time (min)	Distance (ft)	
	Kate	Paco
0	0	90
1	8	98
4	32	122
5	40	130

STEP 1 Find the rate.

Rate: _____

STEP 2 Compare the values.

_____ is always _____ feet ahead of _____.

STEP 3 Write the equations.

Kate: _____

Paco: _____

> **Solve the problem.**

Two interior designers offer different starting prices with the same daily rate. Express Amir's and Bruce's earnings with equations.

Time (days)	Earnings ($)	
	Amir	Bruce
0	0	200
1	600	800
2	1200	1400
5	3000	3200

Rate: $_____

Bruce always earns $_____ more than _____.

Amir: _____

Bruce: _____

> **Explain the similarities and differences between the two equations.**

The equations are similar because _____

The equations are different because _____

_____

_____

TOPIC 3

TOPIC 2

TOPIC 1

SCORE ⓪ ① ②

0 = Incorrect or No Response
1 = Partial Response
2 = Complete and Accurate

Write a Linear Equation From a Description

BLOCK 6

> **WORKED EXAMPLE**

Erica, a web editor, is paid $1000 to create content on a website. She makes an extra $0.50 every time someone clicks on an ad. Write an equation to model the situation.

STEP 1 Identify the variables.

___a___ represents the number of clicked ads.

___e___ represents Erica's earnings.

STEP 2 Identify the initial value.

Initial value: $ _1000_

STEP 3 Find the rate.

Rate: $ _0.50 per ad_

STEP 4 Write the equation.

Equation: _e = 0.50a + 1000_

> **TRY IT**

1 Akeem, an economist, advises his clients to invest in a stock selling for $10 a share. The share price is growing by $0.75 per week. Write an equation to represent the share price for any number of weeks.

w represents the number of weeks.

s represents the stock.

Initial value: $_____

Rate: $_____

Equation: $s =$ _____$w +$ _____

> **GUIDED LEARNING**

2 Kayla, a restaurant owner, donates $300 to charity on her opening day. Each week, she donates $30 more. Write an equation to represent Kayla's total donations for any number of weeks.

STEP 1 Identify the variables.

_____ represents the _____

_____ represents the _____

STEP 2 Identify the initial value.

Initial value: $_____

STEP 3 Find the rate.

Rate: $_____

STEP 4 Write the equation.

Equation: _____

❯ PRACTICE

3

A home Internet plan has an activation fee of $100. Each month of unlimited service costs $50. Write an equation to model the cost of the Internet plan.

STEP 1 Identify the variables.

_____ represents the

_____

_____ represents the

_____

STEP 2 Identify the initial value.

Initial value: $_____

STEP 3 Find the rate.

Rate: $_____

STEP 4 Write the equation.

Equation: _____

4

A sales representative sells a salad dressing recipe for $620 and gets an additional $0.15 for each bottle sold. Write an equation to model the total payment.

STEP 1 Identify the variables.

_____ represents the

_____

_____ represents the

_____

STEP 2 Identify the initial value.

Initial value: $_____

STEP 3 Find the rate.

Rate: $_____

STEP 4 Write the equation.

Equation: _____

EXIT Ticket ❯

BLOCK 6

TOPIC 3

❯ **Solve the problem.**

Sasha is renting office space for her flower business. She spends $10,000 on office supplies, such as flowers, seeds, and computers. The monthly rent is $2000. Write an equation to model the situation.

Equation: _____

❯ *Select all that apply.*
Which of these statements are true?

❑ The rate is $10,000 and the initial value is $2000.

❑ The rate is $2000 and the initial value is $10,000.

❑ An equation that models Sasha's expenses is $s = 2000m + 10{,}000$.

❑ In 5 months, Sasha will spend $20,000.

TOPIC 2

TOPIC 1

SCORE ⓪ ① ②

0 = Incorrect or No Response
1 = Partial Response
2 = Complete and Accurate

RULES
Equation Dash
(Level 1)

When finding the sum, I make sure the positive number is greater than the negative.

What You Need
- *mSpace* pages 58–61
- Counters

How to Play
- Each combination of an expression and *x*-value may be used only once per game.
- When *y* is negative, go back that number of spaces.
- Players may land on the same space.
- Players check each other's work.

How to Win
- The first player to reach the finish line wins.
- Players must land precisely at the finish mark to win.

> HOW TO PLAY

STEP 1 Choose an expression and an *x*-value.

PLAYER A			
EXPRESSION	x-VALUE	SUBSTITUTION	NUMBER OF SPACES
$x - 15$	20		

STEP 2 Substitute the value of *x* into the expression.

PLAYER A			
EXPRESSION	x-VALUE	SUBSTITUTION	NUMBER OF SPACES
$x - 15$	20	$20 - 15$	

STEP 3 Evaluate the expression and move your counter the same number of spaces on the board.

PLAYER A			
EXPRESSION	x-VALUE	SUBSTITUTION	NUMBER OF SPACES
$x - 15$	20	$20 - 15 = 5$	5

STEP 4 Trade turns. Player B repeat Steps 1–3.

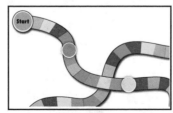

PLAYER B			
EXPRESSION	x-VALUE	SUBSTITUTION	NUMBER OF SPACES
$\frac{3}{4}x$	16	$\frac{3}{4} \cdot 16 = \frac{48}{4}$	12

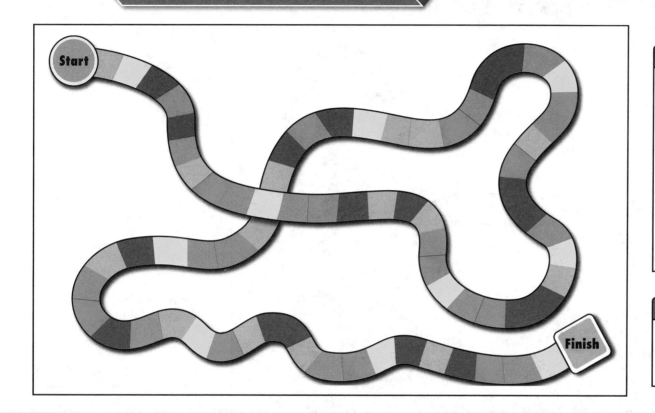

EXPRESSIONS

$x - 15$	$\dfrac{1}{2}x$
$\dfrac{1}{4}x$	$x - 5$
$\dfrac{3}{4}x$	$12 - x$
$\dfrac{3}{2}x$	$(-18) + x$
$x + (-1)$	$20 - x$

x-VALUES

4	8	12
16	20	24

PLAYER A

EXPRESSION	x-VALUE	SUBSTITUTION	NUMBER OF SPACES

PLAYER B

EXPRESSION	x-VALUE	SUBSTITUTION	NUMBER OF SPACES

Start

Finish

RECORDING SHEET
Equation Dash (Level 1)

> Players evaluate expressions and check each other's work.

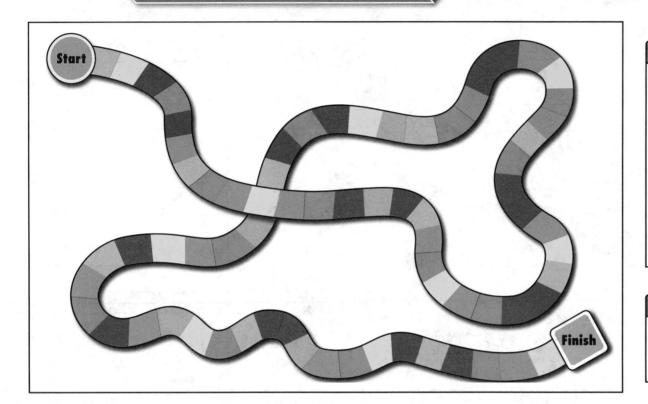

EXPRESSIONS

$x - 15$	$\frac{1}{2}x$
$\frac{1}{4}x$	$x - 5$
$\frac{3}{4}x$	$12 - x$
$\frac{3}{2}x$	$(-18) + x$
$x + (-1)$	$20 - x$

x-VALUES

4	8	12
16	20	24

PLAYER A

EXPRESSION	x-VALUE	SUBSTITUTION	NUMBER OF SPACES

PLAYER B

EXPRESSION	x-VALUE	SUBSTITUTION	NUMBER OF SPACES

FINANCIAL ADVISORS help clients manage their money so that they can meet their savings goals. They may create budgets, suggest investment strategies, and help clients with their retirement planning.

A financial advisor creates the graph below to represent the amount of money a client can save each month.

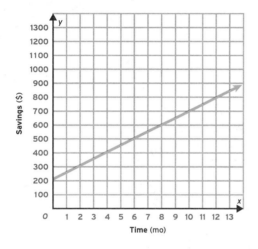

> **Write a linear equation to represent this graph.**

Equation: _____

> **Use the equation to find how much a client would save in 20 months.**

In 20 months, a client would have saved $_____.

EXIT
Ticket

BLOCK
6

TOPIC 3

TOPIC 2

TOPIC 1

> **Answer this question.**

You select the expression 12 − x. What x-value would you choose? Explain.

12 − x

12 − _____ = _____

I would choose _____

because _____

_____

_____

_____

_____

> **What x-value would you not use? Explain.**

I would not choose _____

because _____

_____

_____

_____

_____

_____

_____

SCORE ⓪ ① ②

| 0 = Incorrect or No Response |
| 1 = Partial Response |
| 2 = Complete and Accurate |

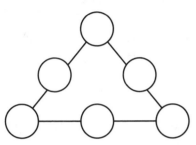

LESSON 1

Brain Teaser

> Fill in the circles with numbers from 1-6 so that each side of the triangle has a sum of 10. You may use each number only once.

> **What is the pattern with the odd and even numbers in your solution?**

The pattern with the odd numbers is that _____

_____

The pattern with the even numbers is that _____

_____

LESSON 2

Who's Right?

> **Mary and Rick found two different answers to the same problem.**

In the triangle below, side *b* is lengthened and side *a* stays the same. Will side *c* become steeper or less steep?

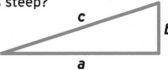

Mary	Rick
Side C will be steeper.	Side C will be less steep.

Who's right? _____

> **Do you agree with Mary or Rick? Explain your reasoning.**

If side *a* is lengthened and side *b* stays the same, _____

_____

I agree with _____ because _____

_____

_____

_____

LESSON 3

Missing Numbers

> **Use the pan balance to complete the equations.**

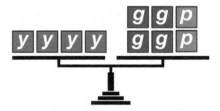

$p = 2g$

$y = \underline{\hspace{1cm}} g$

$y = \underline{\hspace{1cm}} p$

> **How did you begin working on this problem?**

I began working on this problem by _____

_____

_____

_____

_____

LESSON 4

Which Does Not Belong?

> Circle the graph that does not belong.

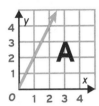
A

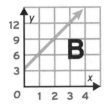
B

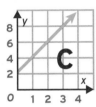
C

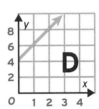
D

> Explain your reasoning.

I think that _____

does not belong because _____

_____

_____

_____

_____

LESSON 5

Brain Arcade

> Select the tiles that complete the equation.

_____ + _____ + _____ = 10.

> How did you know where to place the digits?

I knew where to place the digits

because _____

_____

_____

_____

_____

_____

> In this Topic, you learned how to write a linear equation from a graph, a table, and a description.

What quantities do I need to write a linear equation?

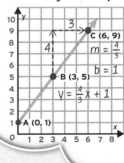

You need the slope and the y-intercept.

$m = \frac{4}{3}$

$b = 1$

$y = \frac{4}{3}x + 1$

A (0, 1)   B (3, 5)   C (6, 9)

Apply Ratio Reasoning to Similar Triangles

> **WORKED EXAMPLE**

Read It! Read the problem.

REAL ESTATE APPRAISER

Izel's driveway has a height of 6 feet. The maximum ratio of a driveway's height to its base is 3:25. What is the length of the base of Izel's driveway?

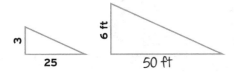

3

25

6 ft

50 ft

Show It! Represent the problem.

Height	Base
3	25
6	50

x 2 ... x 2

Solve It! Solve the problem.

The length of the base of Izel's driveway is __50__ feet.

Check It! Check your work.

> **TRY IT**

1

Read It! Read the problem.

CARPENTER

The height of a skateboard ramp is half the length of its base. Shae builds a ramp with a height of 3.5 feet. What is the length of the base of the ramp?

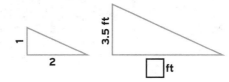

1

2

3.5 ft

☐ ft

Show It! Represent the problem.

Height	Base
1	2
3.5	

Solve It! Solve the problem.

The length of the base of the ramp is _____ feet.

Check It! Check your work.

> **GUIDED LEARNING**

2

Read It! Read the problem.

CONTRACTOR

The ratio of the height to the base of handicap-accessible ramps is 1:20. Kim builds a ramp with a height of 0.5 feet. What is the length of the base of the ramp?

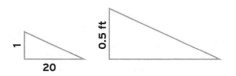

1

20

0.5 ft

Show It! Represent the problem.

Height	Base

Solve It! Solve the problem.

The length of the base of the ramp is _____ feet.

Check It! Check your work.

BLOCK 6

> **PRACTICE**

3

INTERIOR DESIGNER

The ratio of the height to the base of a staircase is 3:5. Mila designs a staircase with a height of 15 feet. What is the length of the base of Mila's staircase?

Height	Base

The length of the base of Mila's staircase is _____ feet.

4

EVENT PLANNER

The ratio of the height to the base of a hill in a speed hiking competition is 1:5. There is a hill with a height of 50 feet and a base of 300 feet. Can this hill be used for the competition?

Height	Base

This hill can / cannot be used for the competition because

_____

_____

_____

_____

EXIT Ticket

BLOCK **6**

> *Select all that apply.*

The ratio of the height to the base of a skateboard kicker ramp must be 1:4.

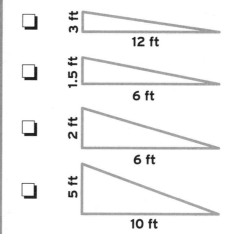

☐ 3 ft — 12 ft

☐ 1.5 ft — 6 ft

☐ 2 ft — 6 ft

☐ 5 ft — 10 ft

TOPIC 3

TOPIC 2

TOPIC 1

SCORE ⓪ ① ②

0 = Incorrect or No Response
1 = Partial Response
2 = Complete and Accurate

LESSON 2
CONCEPT

Determine Slope to Find Rate

> WORKED EXAMPLE

> TRY IT

> GUIDED LEARNING

Nik is starting a tutoring business. He charges a $150 enrollment fee. What is Nik's hourly tutoring rate?

STEP 1 Label the change in each direction.

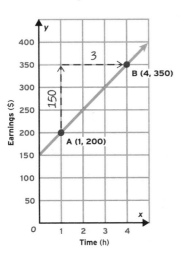

STEP 2 Find the change in one variable.

Change in y: $350 - 200 = 150$

STEP 3 Find the change in the other variable.

Change in x: $4 - 1 = 3$

STEP 4 Find the slope and the rate.

Slope: $\left(\frac{\text{change in } y}{\text{change in } x}\right) = \frac{150}{3}$

$= 50$

Nik's hourly tutoring rate is $\underline{50}$.

1

Liv, an accountant, is choosing between two Internet plans for her company. Both plans charge a $10 installation fee. Which plan charges a lower monthly rate?

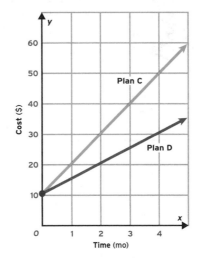

Plan _____ charges a lower monthly rate.

2

Adam is launching a movie-streaming website, Webpix. Webpix charges customers a one-time $20 sign-up fee. What is the monthly membership rate?

STEP 1 Label the change in each direction.

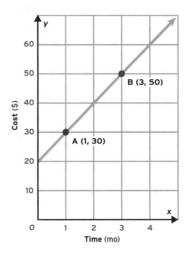

STEP 2 Find the change in one variable.

Change in _____: _____

STEP 3 Find the change in the other variable.

Change in _____: _____

STEP 4 Find the slope and the rate.

Slope: $\left(\frac{\text{change in } y}{\text{change in } x}\right) =$

Webpix charges a monthly membership rate of $_____.

slope (n) a measure of the steepness of a line

> **PRACTICE**

3

Nicole, a babysitter, charges $10 plus an hourly rate. What is Nicole's hourly rate for babysitting?

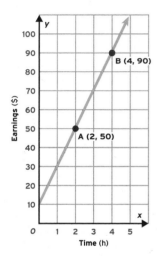

Change in _____: _____

Change in _____: _____

Slope: $\left(\frac{\text{change in } y}{\text{change in } x}\right)$ =

Nicole's hourly babysitting rate is $_____.

4

Sandy, a salon owner, earns $50 per day plus a fee for each haircut. What is Sandy's rate per haircut?

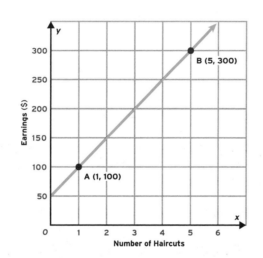

Change in _____: _____

Change in _____: _____

Slope: $\left(\frac{\text{change in } y}{\text{change in } x}\right)$ =

Sandy's rate per haircut is $_____.

EXIT Ticket

> **Solve the problem.**

Mike, an electrician, charges an hourly rate plus a base fee of $100. What is the hourly rate Mike charges?

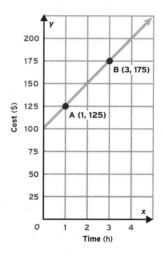

Change in _____: _____

Change in _____: _____

Slope:

Mike's hourly rate is $_____.

> **How did you use change in y and change in x to find your answer?**

To find my answer, I _____

_____

_____

_____

BLOCK **6**

TOPIC 3

TOPIC 2

TOPIC 1

> WORKED EXAMPLE

> TRY IT

> GUIDED LEARNING

BLOCK 6

Demonstrate that the slope of the line $y = \frac{3}{2}x + 3$ is constant.

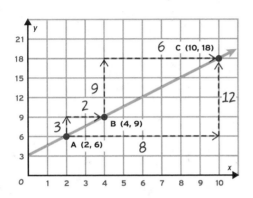

$$\text{Slope} = \frac{\text{change in } y}{\text{change in } x}$$

STEP 1 Find the slope between points A and B.

A and B: $\frac{3}{2}$

STEP 2 Find the slope between points B and C.

B and C: $\frac{9}{6} = \frac{3}{2}$

STEP 3 Find the slope between points A and C.

A and C: $\frac{12}{8} = \frac{3}{2}$

The slope of the line $y = \frac{3}{2}x + 3$ is always $\underline{\frac{3}{2}}$.

1

Find the slope between the points A and B and points B and C. Then, describe the relationships between the slopes.

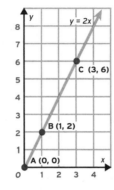

$$\text{Slope} = \frac{\text{change in } y}{\text{change in } x}$$

Slope between points A and B:

Slope between points B and C:

The slopes are equivalent / not equivalent.

2

Demonstrate that the slope of the line $y = \frac{1}{2}x + 2$ is constant.

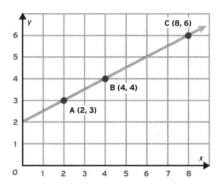

$$\text{Slope} = \frac{\text{change in } y}{\text{change in } x}$$

STEP 1 Find the slope between points A and B.

A and B:

STEP 2 Find the slope between points B and C.

B and C:

STEP 3 Find the slope between points A and C.

A and C:

The slope of the line $y = \frac{1}{2}x + 2$ is always _____.

---

slope *(n)* a measure of the steepness of a line

equivalent fractions *(n)* two or more fractions that name the same part of a whole

> **PRACTICE**

3
Demonstrate that the slope of the line $y = x$ is constant.

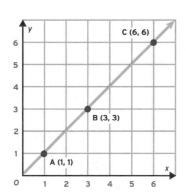

$$\text{Slope} = \frac{\text{change in } y}{\text{change in } x}$$

STEP 1 Find the slope between points A and B.

A and B:

STEP 2 Find the slope between points B and C.

B and C:

STEP 3 Find the slope between points A and C.

A and C:

The slope of the line $y = x$ is always _____.

4
Demonstrate that the slope of the line $y = \frac{2}{3}x + 1$ is constant.

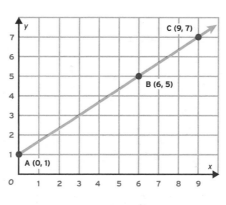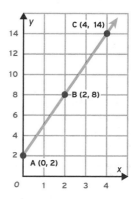

$$\text{Slope} = \frac{\text{change in } y}{\text{change in } x}$$

STEP 1 Find the slope between points A and B.

A and B:

STEP 2 Find the slope between points B and C.

B and C:

STEP 3 Find the slope between points A and C.

A and C:

The slope of the line $y = \frac{2}{3}x + 1$ is always _____.

> **Solve the problem.**

Demonstrate that the slope of the line $y = 3x + 2$ is constant.

A and B:

B and C:

A and C:

The slope of the line $y = 3x + 2$ is always _____.

> **How can you determine if a line has a constant slope?**

I can determine if a line has a constant slope by _____ _____ _____

SCORE ⓪ ① ②
0 = Incorrect or No Response
1 = Partial Response
2 = Complete and Accurate

BLOCK
6

TOPIC 3

TOPIC 2

TOPIC 1

Analyze a Line to Write an Equation

> **WORKED EXAMPLE**

Represent the line with an equation, and determine whether (15, 12) is a solution to the equation.

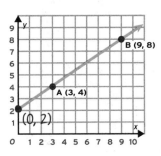

$$\text{Slope} = \frac{\text{change in } y}{\text{change in } x}$$

Equation: $y = mx + b$

STEP 1 Find the slope, m.

$$m = \frac{8-4}{9-3} = \frac{4}{6} = \frac{2}{3}$$

STEP 2 Find the y-intercept.

$b = 2$

STEP 3 Write the equation of the line.

$y = \frac{2}{3}x + 2$

STEP 4 Verify another solution to the equation.

$12 = \frac{2}{3}(15) + 2$

$12 = 10 + 2$

$12 = 12$

(15, 12) (is)/ is not a solution to the equation.

> **TRY IT**

1 Pamela is planning a fundraising event. The cost per person is $20. Write an equation that models the total amount of money raised.

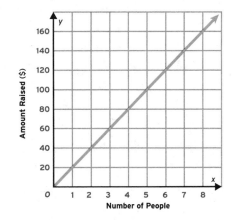

Equation: _____

> **GUIDED LEARNING**

2 Represent the line with an equation, and determine whether (8, 6) is a solution to the equation.

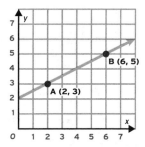

$$\text{Slope} = \frac{\text{change in } y}{\text{change in } x}$$

Equation: $y = mx + b$

STEP 1 Find the slope, m.

STEP 2 Find the y-intercept.

STEP 3 Write the equation of the line.

STEP 4 Verify another solution to the equation.

(8, 6) is / is not a solution to the equation.

y-intercept *(n)* a point where a graph crosses the vertical axis

solution *(n)* any ordered pair of values that make an equation true

› PRACTICE

3

Represent the line with an equation, and determine whether (5, 19) is a solution to the equation.

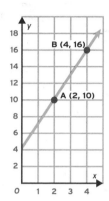

Slope = $\dfrac{\text{change in } y}{\text{change in } x}$

Equation: $y = mx + b$

STEP 1 Find the slope, *m*.

STEP 2 Find the *y*-intercept.

STEP 3 Write the equation of the line.

STEP 4 Verify another solution to the equation.

(5, 19) is / is not a solution to the equation.

4

Represent the line with an equation, and determine whether (8, 13) is a solution to the equation.

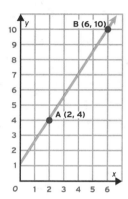

Slope = $\dfrac{\text{change in } y}{\text{change in } x}$

Equation: $y = mx + b$

STEP 1 Find the slope, *m*.

STEP 2 Find the *y*-intercept.

STEP 3 Write the equation of the line.

STEP 4 Verify another solution to the equation.

(8, 13) is / is not a solution to the equation.

› Solve the problem.

Represent the line with an equation, and determine whether (20, 15) is a solution to the equation.

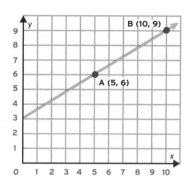

› How did you verify the ordered pair?

I verified the ordered pair by

_____

_____

_____

_____

_____

_____

TOPIC 2

TOPIC 1

SCORE ⓪ ① ②   0 = Incorrect or No Response
1 = Partial Response
2 = Complete and Accurate

Use Reasoning With Equations

RULES
Equation Dash
(Level 2)

Before I choose an *x*-value, I estimate what number I need to land on a space.

What You Need

- *mSpace* pages 72–75
- Counters

How to Play

- Each combination of an equation and *x*-value may be used only once per game.
- When *y* is negative, go back that number of spaces.
- Players may land on the same space.
- Players check each other's work.

How to Win

- The first player to reach the finish line wins.
- Players must land precisely at the finish mark to win.

STEP 1 **Choose an equation and an *x*-value.**

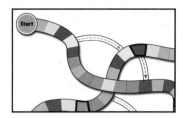

PLAYER A			
EQUATION	x-VALUE	SUBSTITUTION	y-VALUE
$y = \frac{1}{2}x + 2$	10		

STEP 2 **Substitute the value of *x* into the equation.**

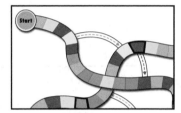

PLAYER A			
EQUATION	x-VALUE	SUBSTITUTION	y-VALUE
$y = \frac{1}{2}x + 2$	10	$\frac{1}{2}(10) + 2 = 5 + 2$	

STEP 3 **Find the value of *y*, and move your counter the same number of spaces on the board.**

PLAYER A			
EQUATION	x-VALUE	SUBSTITUTION	y-VALUE
$y = \frac{1}{2}x + 2$	10	$\frac{1}{2}(10) + 2 = 5 + 2$	7

STEP 4 **Trade turns. Player B repeat Steps 1–3.**

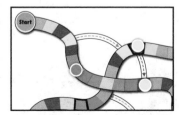

PLAYER B			
EQUATION	x-VALUE	SUBSTITUTION	y-VALUE
$y = 2x + (-12)$	8	$2(8) + (-12) = 16 + (-12)$	4

RECORDING SHEET

Equation Dash (Level 2)

> Players substitute *x*-values and check each other's work.

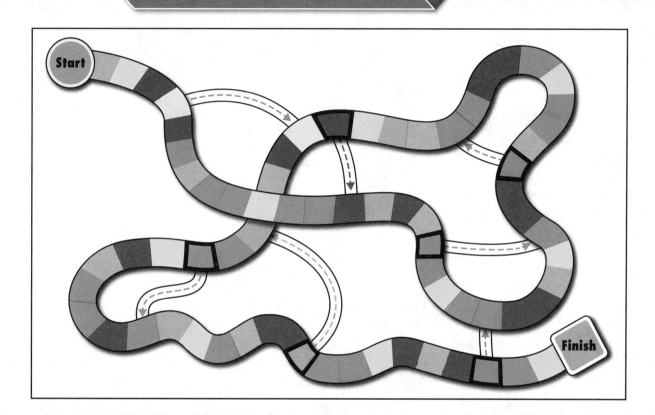

EQUATIONS

$y = x + (-10)$

$y = 0.5x + 4$

$y = \frac{1}{2}x + 2$

$y = \frac{1}{2}x + (-3)$

$y = 3x + (-16)$

$y = 2x + (-12)$

x-VALUES

2	4	6
8	10	12

PLAYER A

EQUATION	x-VALUE	SUBSTITUTION	y-VALUE

PLAYER B

EQUATION	x-VALUE	SUBSTITUTION	y-VALUE

RECORDING SHEET
Equation Dash (Level 2)

> Players substitute x-values and check each other's work.

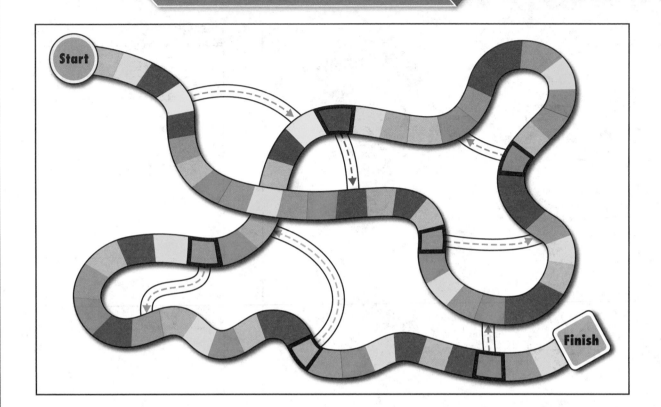

EQUATIONS

$y = x + (-10)$

$y = 0.5x + 4$

$y = \frac{1}{2}x + 2$

$y = \frac{1}{2}x + (-3)$

$y = 3x + (-16)$

$y = 2x + (-12)$

x-VALUES

2	4	6
8	10	12

PLAYER A				
EQUATION	x-VALUE	SUBSTITUTION	y-VALUE

PLAYER B				
EQUATION	x-VALUE	SUBSTITUTION	y-VALUE

RESTAURATEURS are owners and often managers of restaurants. They may hire people to order and keep track of the food, supplies, and equipment. Other responsibilities include training and scheduling employees.

The table shows a list of food items a restaurateur needs to order. Represent the cost of each item as an equation.

FOOD	COST (per 10 lb)	EQUATION
Steak	$60	$y = 60x$
Chicken	$20	
Pork	$30	
Lamb	$50	

> **Find the cost of each item when 5 orders are placed.**

Steak: _____

Chicken: _____

Pork: _____

Lamb: _____

> **Use the cost from above to graph the function of each item.**

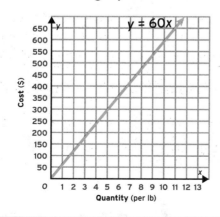

EXIT
Ticket

BLOCK
6

TOPIC 3

> **Solve the problem.**

Draw lines to match the *x*-value that produces the given *y*-value in the equations.

$11 = 5x + 1$	$x = 4$
$14 = 4x + 2$	$x = 5$
$16 = 3x + 4$	$x = 2$
$15 = 2x + 5$	$x = 3$

TOPIC 2

> **Choose an equation. How would you solve it using mental math?**

Using mental math, I can solve _____

_____

_____

TOPIC 1

_____

_____

Brain Teaser

> Each of the digits from 1–4 must occur once in each row and once in each column. What number will occupy the last square?

1		2	
2	3		
			4
		☐	

The number in the last square is _____.

> What steps did you take to solve this problem?

The first step I took was to _____

_____

_____ Then, I _____

_____

_____

Missing Numbers

> Place the digits 2, 3, 4, 5, and 6 in the circles so that the horizontal and vertical sums are equal to 12.

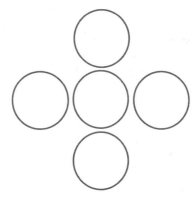

> How do you know your answer is correct?

I know my answer is correct because _____

_____

_____

_____

Who's Right?

> Bobby and Jamal wrote different equations to represent the line.

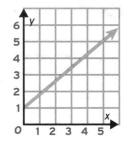

Bobby   Jamal

$y = \frac{4}{5}x + 1$ $y = \frac{5}{4}x + 1$

Who's right? _____

> What error did Jamal make?

Jamal's error was _____

_____

_____

_____

_____

LESSON 4

Find the Pattern

> Use the table to find the pattern.

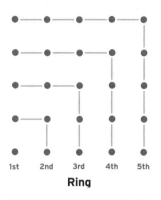

1st 2nd 3rd 4th 5th

Ring

Ring	Dots
1	
2	
3	
4	
5	
6	
7	

> What expression can you write to find the number of dots in the 100th ring?

The expression I can write is _____

_____

_____

_____

_____

LESSON 5

Build It

> Build an equation using 3 of the numbers listed.

$$12 = \underline{\quad} \cdot \underline{\quad} + \underline{\quad}$$

| $\frac{1}{2}$ | 2 | 3 | 6 | 20 |

> How did you begin solving this problem?

I began solving this problem by ___

_____

_____

_____

> In this Topic, you learned how to find the value of *x* and find the value of *y* in a linear equation.

How do I find the value of *y*?

You substitute the *x*-value and simplify.

Solve Problems With Slope

> WORKED EXAMPLE

Lisa, a park manager, represented a roller-coaster section on the graph below. Adjust the section to have a 20-foot base and a slope of 4.

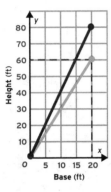

Base (ft)

STEP 1 Analyze the current slope.

$\frac{\text{height}}{\text{base}}\left(\frac{\text{change in } y}{\text{change in } x}\right): \frac{60}{20} = 3$

STEP 2 Find the new measurement.

$\frac{\text{height}}{\text{base}}\left(\frac{\text{change in } y}{\text{change in } x}\right): \frac{80}{20} = 4$

STEP 3 Graph the adjustment.

STEP 4 Explain your solution.

To (increase) / decrease the slope, the height _increases from 60 feet to 80 feet_ , and the base _remains 20 feet_

_____.

> TRY IT

1 Carrie's apartment building ramp has a 2-foot height and a 4-foot base. The new building code says the ramp must have a 1:4 height-to-base ratio. How can Carrie adjust her ramp's base to meet the new code?

Carrie can adjust the ramp's base by

_____

> GUIDED LEARNING

2 Ji, a safety inspector, represented a slide on the graph below. Adjust Ji's slide to have an 80-foot height and a slope of 2.

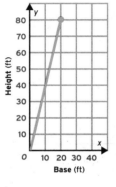

Base (ft)

STEP 1 Analyze the current slope.

$\frac{\text{height}}{\text{base}}\left(\frac{\text{change in } y}{\text{change in } x}\right):$

STEP 2 Find the new measurement.

$\frac{\text{height}}{\text{base}}\left(\frac{\text{change in } y}{\text{change in } x}\right):$

STEP 3 Graph the adjustment.

STEP 4 Explain your solution.

To increase / decrease the slope, the height _____

_____, and the base

_____

_____.

ratio *(n)* a comparison of related numbers or quantities

slope *(n)* a measure of steepness of a line

> PRACTICE

3 Monica, a store manager, represented the dimensions of a display case on the graph below. Adjust the case to have a 10-inch depth and a slope of 2.5.

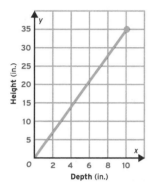
Depth (in.)

To increase / decrease the slope,

the depth _____

_____, and the height

_____

_____.

4 Paco, a fireman, represented the extension of a ladder on the graph below. Adjust the ladder to have a 60-foot height and a slope of 6.

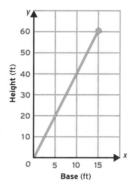
Base (ft)

To increase / decrease the slope,

the height _____

_____, and the base

_____

_____.

> *Select all that apply.*

Lucia's firm is working on a highway project. An on-ramp has a height of 3 feet and a horizontal distance of 25 feet. How can Lucia adjust the ramp to have a slope of 3:50?

☐ Increase the horizontal distance to 50 feet.

☐ Increase the height to 6 feet.

☐ Decrease the horizontal distance to 12.5 feet.

☐ Decrease the height to 1.5 feet.

In problems involving slope, there are multiple ways I can adjust the slope by manipulating the measurements.

TOPIC 3

TOPIC 2

TOPIC 1

SCORE ⓪ ① ②

0 = Incorrect or No Response
1 = Partial Response
2 = Complete and Accurate

> WORKED EXAMPLE

> TRY IT

> GUIDED LEARNING

Jamal, a personal trainer, charges a sign-up fee of $50 plus $25 per session. What is the cost to hire Jamal for 5 sessions?

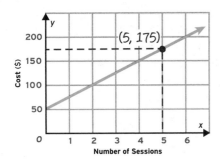

STEP 1 Make an estimate.

Estimate: between $150 and $200

STEP 2 Identify the parts of the equation.

Cost: __y__

Rate per session: $__25__

Sessions: __x__

Sign-up fee: $__50__

Equation: y = 25x + 50

STEP 3 Find the value of *y.*

y = 25(5) + 50

y = 125 + 50

y = 175

The cost to hire Jamal for 5 personal training sessions is $175.

STEP 4 Verify the solution.

---

1 The cost to rent a bicycle is $5.00 per hour. How much will it cost to rent a bicycle for 3 hours?

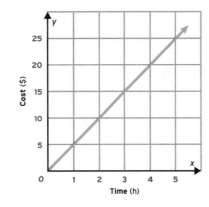

The cost to rent a bicycle for 3 hours is $_____.

---

2 Ryan charges a fixed fee of $25 for each party he caters plus $10 per person. What is the cost to have Ryan cater a party with 6 people?

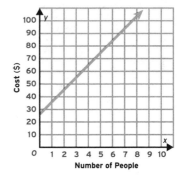

STEP 1 Make an estimate.

Estimate: _____

STEP 2 Identify the parts of the equation.

Cost: _____

Rate per person: $_____

People: _____

Fixed fee: $_____

Equation: _____

STEP 3 Find the value of *y.*

The cost to have Ryan cater a party with 6 people is $_____.

STEP 4 Verify the solution.

> PRACTICE

3
A cell phone plan charges $45 for activation plus $20 per month. What is the charge if a plan is activated for 3 months?

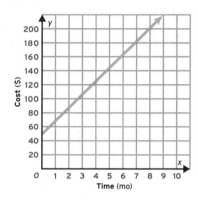

Estimate: _____

Cost: $_____

Activation fee: $_____

Months: _____

Cost per month: $_____

Equation: _____

The cost of a cell phone plan for 3 months is $_____.

4
A website hosting company charges $500 for developing a website and $75 for monthly maintenance. What are the fees for a new website and 6 months of maintenance?

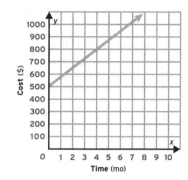

Estimate: _____

Total cost: $_____

Developing fee: $_____

Months: _____

Cost per month: $_____

Equation: _____

The cost of a new website and 6 months of maintenance is $_____.

EXIT Ticket

> Solve the problem.

Jada is launching her new website, Songs B Heard. To join, there is a one-time fee of $50 plus $0.25 per song download. How much will it cost to download 100 songs?

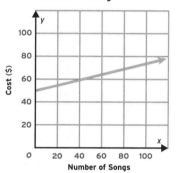

The cost to download 100 songs from Songs B Heard is $_____.

> If Zach has $100, how many songs can he download?

Zach can download _____ songs because _____

_____

_____

_____

_____

SCORE ⓪ ① ②   0 = Incorrect or No Response
1 = Partial Response
2 = Complete and Accurate

Estimate a Solution to a Linear Equation

> WORKED EXAMPLE

> TRY IT

> GUIDED LEARNING

Kim, a restaurant owner, orders produce for delivery. She pays a $75 delivery fee plus $1.25 per pound of produce. How many pounds of produce can Kim purchase with $100?

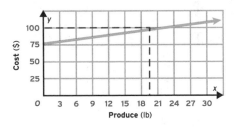

STEP 1 Make an estimate.

about 21 pounds

STEP 2 Identify the parts of the equation.

Cost: __y__

Rate per pound: $ _1.25_

Pounds: __x__

Fixed fee: $_75_

Equation: _y = 1.25x + 75_

STEP 3 Find the value of y.

Equation: y = 1.25x + 75
$$y = 1.25(21) + 75$$
$$y = 26.25 + 75$$
$$y = 101.25$$

STEP 4 Reason about your estimate.

x = 20
I need to decrease my estimate.

---

1 Studio equipment rents for $27 per hour plus a $200 deposit fee. How many hours of equipment rental can Sam purchase for $350?

x	27x + 200
0	200
1	227
2	254
3	281
4	308
5	335
6	362

Sam can purchase _____ hours of equipment rental for $350.

---

2 Evan, a DJ, charges a $200 fee plus $24 per hour. How many hours can Evan work for $500?

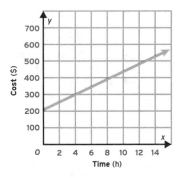

STEP 1 Make an estimate.

STEP 2 Identify the parts of the equation.

Cost: _____

Rate per hour: $_____

Hours: _____

Fixed fee: $_____

Equation: _____

STEP 3 Find the value of y.

Equation:

STEP 4 Reason about your estimate.

linear equation *(n)* an equation whose graph is a straight line

> **PRACTICE**

3
An airport Internet service provider charges a $3 connection fee plus $0.25 per minute. How many minutes of Internet access can be bought for $8?

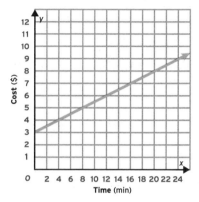

STEP 1 Make an estimate.

STEP 2 Identify parts of the equation.

Cost: _____

Rate: $_____

Minutes: _____

Fixed fee: $_____

Equation: _____

STEP 3 Find the value of *y*.

STEP 4 Reason about your estimate.

4
A prepaid cell phone plan charges $0.35 per call plus $0.08 per minute. How many minutes can Nicole use for $1.20?

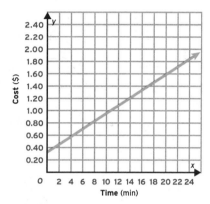

STEP 1 Make an estimate.

STEP 2 Identify parts of the equation.

Cost: _____

Rate: $_____

Minutes: _____

Fixed fee: $_____

Equation: _____

STEP 3 Find the value of *y*.

STEP 4 Reason about your estimate.

> **Find the error in the equation and fix the math.**

Jack, a tutor, charges a $20 flat fee plus $10.25 per hour.

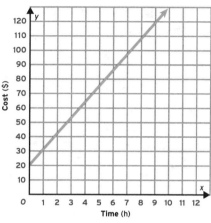

Equation:

$y = 20x + 10.25$

> **Explain the error and how you fixed it.**

_____
_____
_____
_____
_____
_____

TOPIC 3

TOPIC 2

TOPIC 1

SCORE ⓪ ① ②
0 = Incorrect or No Response
1 = Partial Response
2 = Complete and Accurate

LESSON 4

Find the Value of *x* in a Linear Equation

> **WORKED EXAMPLE**

A new gaming app costs $3, plus $2 for each in-app purchase. The app purchases are represented by the equation $y = 2x + 3$. If Nima has $27, how many in-app purchases can she make?

STEP 1 Model the problem.

The variable that represents the total cost is __y__.

The variable that represents the number of in-app purchases is __x__.

STEP 2 Substitute the value of *y*.

$y = 2x + 3$

$27 = 2x + 3$

STEP 3 Find the value that makes the equation true.

$27 = 2x + 3$

$27 - 3 = 2x + 3 - 3$

$24 = 2x$

STEP 4 Find the value of *x*.

$24 = 2x$

$\frac{24}{2} = \frac{2x}{2}$

$12 = x$ or $x = 12$

Nima can make __12__ in-app purchases with $27.

> **TRY IT**

1

Tom's recording studio charges $150 for equipment plus $27.50 per hour for a room rental. How much studio time can a band rent for $250?

Time (h)	Total Cost ($)
0	150
1	177.50
2	
3	
4	

A band can rent _____ hours of studio time for $250.

> **GUIDED LEARNING**

2

Julie designs and sells T-shirts. Each T-shirt sells for $3 plus an $8 delivery fee, which is represented by the equation $y = 3x + 8$. How many T-shirts can Julie sell for $50?

STEP 1 Model the problem.

The variable that represents the _____ is _____.

The variable that represents the _____ is _____.

STEP 2 Substitute the value of *y*.

STEP 3 Find the value that makes the equation true.

STEP 4 Find the value of *x*.

Julie sells _____ T-shirts for $50.

equation (n) a mathematical sentence that states that two quantities or expressions are equal

substitute (n) to replace a variable in an expression with a number

> PRACTICE

3

A vending machine owner sells 40 snacks per day. The vending machine owner has sold 200 snacks so far, which can be represented by the equation $y = 40x + 200$. How many days will it take to sell 500 snacks?

STEP 1 Model the problem.

The variable that represents the

_____

is _____.

The variable that represents the

_____ is _____.

STEP 2 Substitute the value of y.

STEP 3 Find the value that makes the equation true.

STEP 4 Find the value of x.

It will take _____ days to sell 500 snacks.

4

A start-up company collects $200 per day from investors. It already has $6500 in savings, which can be represented by the equation $y = 200x + 6500$. How many days does the company need until it has $10,000 altogether?

STEP 1 Model the problem.

The variable that represents the

_____ is _____.

The variable that represents the

_____ is _____.

STEP 2 Substitute the value of y.

STEP 3 Find the value that makes the equation true.

STEP 4 Find the value of x.

The company needs _____ days until it has $10,000 altogether.

EXIT Ticket

BLOCK **6**

TOPIC 3

> Solve the problem.
Lori, a personal trainer, earns $45 per hour. She already earned $90 from her first client. How many hours will she have to work altogether to earn $225?

TOPIC 2

Lori will have to work _____ hours to earn $225.

> Explain how you found your answer.

_____

_____

_____

TOPIC 1

_____

_____

_____

SCORE ⓪ ① ②

0 = Incorrect or No Response
1 = Partial Response
2 = Complete and Accurate

LESSON 5
PROBLEM SOLVING

ANCHOR VIDEO CONNECTION

As the Anchor Video shows, you can use linear relationships to make predictions in a business plan.

BLOCK 6

Determine Projections With Models

> You own a successful restaurant and want to expand to a second location. To expand, you will need to invest $200,000. You need to know if this investment will increase your savings over time.

Savings Projections

- Your current savings are $200,000.
- With one location, your projected annual savings are $75,000.
- With two locations, your projected annual savings are $100,000 altogether.

A CREATE

Create a table and a graph to represent your savings with each plan.

Time (yr)	Savings ($)	
	1 Location	2 Locations
0		
1		
2		
3		
4		

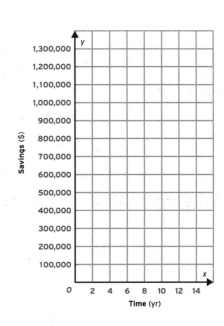

BIG IDEA 1 A linear relationship has a constant rate of change.

BIG IDEA 2 Representing linear relationships with tables, graphs, and equations helps us to find unknown values.

B PREDICT

Write an equation to predict your savings for any number of years with each plan.

y represents _____

x represents _____

1 Location:

2 Locations:

C EXPLAIN

Will your savings be greater in 8 years with 1 or 2 locations? Explain your reasoning.

1 Location	2 Locations

_____

_____

_____

_____

EXIT Ticket

BLOCK
6

TOPIC 3

> **Solve the problem.**

Your goal is to make $1,000,000 as quickly as possible. Should you open another location?

_____

Explain your reasoning.

_____

_____

_____

_____

_____

_____

TOPIC 2

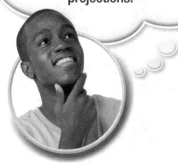

I can model a situation with an equation and use the equation to make projections.

TOPIC 1

SCORE ⓪ ① ②

0 = Incorrect or No Response
1 = Partial Response
2 = Complete and Accurate

Interpreting Linear Equations **87**

> **YOUR JOB**
Artisan

> **YOUR TASK**
Determine your profitability.

ANCHOR VIDEO CONNECTION

As the Anchor Video shows, entrepreneurs use linear relationships to keep track of profits.

Street Fair Sales

> **You create and sell spray-paint T-shirts. To boost your business, you attend a local street fair to sell your T-shirts.**

A EXPLORE

You brought 30 spray-paint T-shirts to the street fair. At the fair, you created 2 additional spray-paint T-shirts per hour. Write an equation and graph the line representing the total number of T-shirts you made.

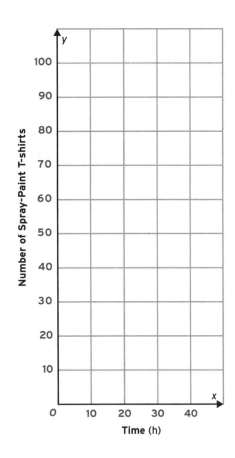

x represents _____

y represents _____

m = _____

b = _____

Equation: _____

At the fair, you sold 30 premade spray-paint T-shirts and took orders for 90 personalized spray-paint T-shirts.

1. **Profit:** Calculate your total cost and revenue to find your total profit.

Revenue $5 per premade spray-paint T-shirt $10 per personalized spray-paint T-shirt	Cost $3 per spray-paint T-shirt	Profit Revenue − Cost = Profit
My revenue is $_____.	My cost is $_____.	My profit is $_____.

2. **Time:** Find the total number of hours you worked for the street fair.

Before	During	After
You made 30 spray-paint T-shirts at a rate of 3 spray-paint T-shirts per hour. How many hours did you work before the street fair?	You made 60 spray-paint T-shirts at a rate of 2 spray-paint T-shirts per hour. How many hours were you at the street fair?	You have 30 orders left to complete. At a rate of 3 spray-paint T-shirts per hour, how many more hours do you need to work?

How many total hours did you work?

3. **Rate:** Find your hourly profit rate using the total profit and number of hours you worked for the fair.

What is your hourly profit?

EXPLAIN You can buy 5 premade T-shirts for $20. Is selling them for $5 each profitable?

_____

_____

REFLECT Create a plan to increase your profit to $15 per hour.

_____

_____

Evaluate

> **Rate how well you and your partner understood and completed each part of the performance task.**

Ranking Scale			
None	Limited	Partial	Thorough
0	1	2	3

A Correctly modeled the situation with an equation and graph.

| Me | 0 | 1 | 2 | 3 |
| Partner | 0 | 1 | 2 | 3 |

B Accurately responded to all questions.

| Me | 0 | 1 | 2 | 3 |
| Partner | 0 | 1 | 2 | 3 |

C Answered each question thoughtfully.

| Me | 0 | 1 | 2 | 3 |
| Partner | 0 | 1 | 2 | 3 |

EXTEND

If you made and sold more premade spray-paint T-shirts at the fair, how would that affect your hourly rate?

_____

_____

_____

_____

_____

BLOCK 6 **MINDSET STRATEGY**

Reflect on Self-Efficacy
Congratulations! You've completed Block 6 of *MATH 180*.

What's the Buzz?

Tina Wells started her own business at age 16 in New Jersey. Now, as CEO of Buzz Marketing Group, she has 9000 teen consultants she calls "buzzspotters." They help her stay on top of market trends for beauty, fashion, and entertainment. Wells has **self-efficacy**, which is the feeling that you can succeed through your own efforts.

Growing Confidence

As a teenager, Wells submitted reviews of her favorite products to magazines and encouraged her friends to do the same. This grew her confidence to start her own business.

Finding Success

Now companies around the world hire her when they need to know what's trendy. She was named one of *Fast Company*'s most creative people of 2014.

> **How do people's beliefs about themselves affect their success?**

People's beliefs about themselves affect their success by _____

_____

_____

_____

Tina Wells

"Your dreams don't have to have an expiration date."
—Tina Wells

How to Develop Self-Efficacy

> You learn best when you believe in yourself and focus on what you can do to achieve your goals. Here are ways you can stay calm, positive, and motivated.

 Self-Talk: I can succeed! *Focus on how you will confront a challenge, and try not to worry about what could go wrong.*

 Manage Stress: Try taking slow, deep breaths. *If you start to doubt yourself, take slow, deep breaths. This lowers your heart rate and reduces stress.*

 Get Guidance: Find a coach and build a network. *Reach out to people who are working on similar projects for information, ideas, and support.*

Putting It Into Practice

> Write about a challenge that you have taking a math test.

_____

_____

_____

> Explain how you could use each of these strategies to help you to develop your self-efficacy when you take a test.

Self-Talk: When a math question looks hard…	Manage Stress: One approach I will try the next time I struggle on a question is…	Get Guidance: One person who can help me prepare or review is…

VOCABULARY

Additive Identity Property

additive inverse

coordinate plane

factor

order of operations

product

quadrant

quotient

All in Your Head

What if a video game could read your thoughts?

In this Anchor Video, find out how brainwave technology is changing the way that people of all abilities experience entertainment.

Math in Entertainment

In this Block, you will learn how graphs in the plane are used in entertainment.

Choreographers

arrange dance movements and patterns. They teach the dance moves at a slower speed and then increase the number of **beats per minute**.

Music Data Analysts

study and analyze trends in the music industry. Revenue from CD sales has been **declining** for over a decade!

Audio Engineers

use **linear fade-outs** to lower the music sound level at a **constant rate** at the end of a song.

Stage Managers

Recreating the stage with a **floor grid** helps

with the placement of actors and props. The **coordinate system** helps specify locations and determine paths.

Sports Photographers

take fast action photos. A camera's **shutter speed** is **proportional** to the amount of light exposing the picture. Faster-moving sports like motor racing require a faster shutter speed to reduce blurriness.

BLOCK 7

BLOCK 7

Block Preview

> Read the Career Explorations on *mSpace* page 91. Which career interests you the most? Why?

The career that interests me

most is _____

because _____

_____

_____

_____

> How is math used in entertainment?

Math is used in entertainment

_____

_____

_____

_____

Brain Teaser

> Use digits from 1 to 9 to complete the puzzle.

$$\square \times 9 \div \square = 15$$
$$+ \qquad - \qquad \times \qquad -$$
$$3 + \square + 1 = \square$$
$$= \qquad = \qquad = \qquad =$$
$$\square \div \square \times \square = 6$$

> How did you start solving this puzzle?

I started solving this puzzle by ___

_____

_____

_____

_____

Find the Pattern

> Fill in the boxes, and identify the pattern to find the sum.

$$5 + \square + 7$$
$$+ \; \square + 6 + \square$$
$$\overline{}$$
$$12 + 12 + 12 = 36$$
$$5 + 6 + 7 = 36 \div 2$$
$$5 + 6 + 7 = \underline{}$$

> Use this pattern to find the sum of 6, 7, 8, 9, and 10.

$$6 + 7 + 8 + 9 + 10$$
$$+ \square + \square + \square + \square + \square$$
$$\overline{}$$

LESSON 4

Build It

> Fill in the ovals using the numbers -2, $\frac{3}{4}$, 1.5, 2, 3, 8, and 4 so that the product of each line is -12.

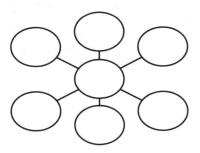

> What number did you choose to place first? Explain.

I chose to place _____ first because _____

_____

_____

LESSON 5

Brain Arcade

> Select the fish with the number that makes the equation true.

$$4 \times (-6) = 12 \times \underline{\hspace{1cm}}$$

> How did you find the missing value in the equation?

I found the missing value by _____

_____

_____

_____

_____

_____

> In this Topic, you generated solutions to an equation in all four quadrants.

How can I find the solution to the equation $y = \frac{1}{2}x$ when $x = -8$?

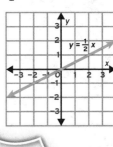

I can't use the graph to generate a solution, but I can substitute the value of x into the equation.

$$y = \frac{1}{2}x$$
$$y = \frac{1}{2} \cdot (-8)$$
$$y = -4$$

$(-8, -4)$ is a solution to $y = \frac{1}{2}x$.

LESSON 1
PROBLEM SOLVING

ANCHOR VIDEO CONNECTION

As the Anchor Video shows, as math and technology advance, the entertainment industry applies the innovations in creative and fun ways.

BLOCK 7

Solve Puzzles With Negative Numbers

> You are a puzzle designer. You are creating the answer key for challenge puzzles in an activity entertainment book.

Challenge puzzles are just like regular puzzles—but they use numbers that have a sum of 0.

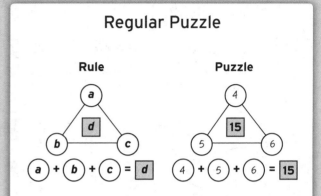

Regular Puzzle

Rule   Puzzle

$a + b + c = d$ $4 + 5 + 6 = 15$

A CREATE

Create two challenge puzzles whose sum is 0.

Puzzle 1

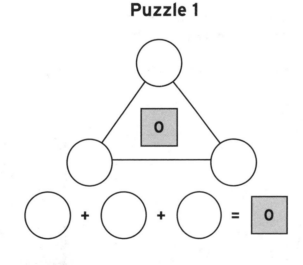

Puzzle 2

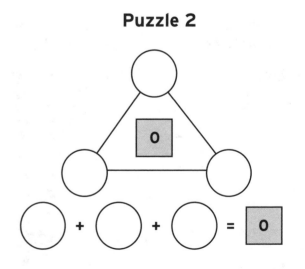

BIG IDEA 1 **Symbolic representations** help to clearly communicate mathematical ideas.

BIG IDEA 2 **Different types of numbers** are necessary to solve a range of problems.

B PREDICT

Describe the pattern in all challenge puzzles that have a sum of 0.

_____

_____

_____

_____

_____

_____

C EXPLAIN

Richard says that challenge puzzles can't be solved without negative numbers. Do you agree or disagree? Explain your reasoning.

_____

_____

_____

_____

_____

_____

_____

EXIT Ticket

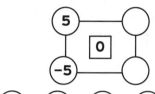

BLOCK **7**

> **Solve the problem.**

Jose is creating a similar puzzle for a newspaper. Complete the puzzle.

$$5 \quad \bigcirc$$
$$\boxed{0}$$
$$-5 \quad \bigcirc$$

$$\bigcirc 5 + \bigcirc{-5} + \bigcirc + \bigcirc = \boxed{0}$$

> **Describe all the values that solve the puzzle.**

_____

_____

_____

_____

TOPIC 3

TOPIC 2

TOPIC 1

I can use the Additive Identity Property $(3 + 0 = 3)$ and the additive inverse $(3 + (-3) = 0)$ to solve these puzzles.

SCORE ⓪ ① ②   0 = Incorrect or No Response
1 = Partial Response
2 = Complete and Accurate

Plot Points in Four Quadrants

> WORKED EXAMPLE

Build a rectangle in the coordinate plane.

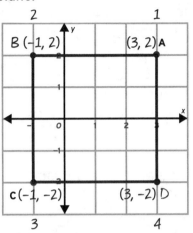

Point	(x, y)
A	(3, 2)
B	(−1, 2)
C	(−1, −2)
D	(3, −2)

STEP 1 Find the coordinates of point A.

STEP 2 Find the coordinates of point C.

STEP 3 Plot point B.

STEP 4 Complete the rectangle.

> TRY IT

1 Plot point B on the graph. Then, complete the table.

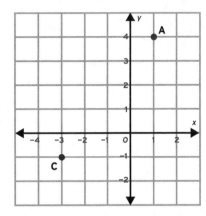

Point	(x, y)
A	
B	(−3, 4)
C	

> GUIDED LEARNING

2 Build a rectangle in the coordinate plane.

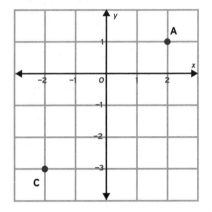

Point	(x, y)
A	
B	(−2, 1)
C	
D	

STEP 1 Find the coordinates of point A.

STEP 2 Find the coordinates of point C.

STEP 3 Plot point B.

STEP 4 Complete the rectangle.

BLOCK 7

EXIT Ticket

BLOCK 7

> **PRACTICE**

3
Build a rectangle in the coordinate plane.

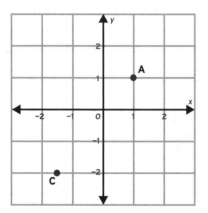

Point	(x, y)
A	
B	(−1.5, 1)
C	
D	

4
Build a rectangle in the coordinate plane.

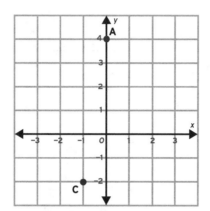

Point	(x, y)
A	
B	(−1, 4)
C	
D	

5
Build a rectangle in the coordinate plane.

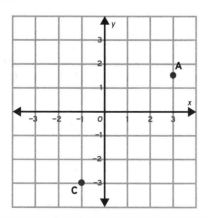

6
Build a rectangle in the coordinate plane.

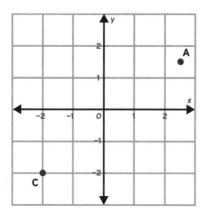

> **Solve the problem.**

Build a rectangle in the coordinate plane.

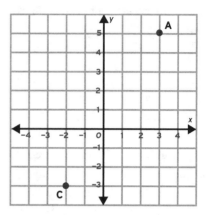

Point	(x, y)
A	
B	(−2, 5)
C	
D	

> **Can a point in the first quadrant of the coordinate plane have a negative coordinate? Explain.**

A point in the first quadrant can / can't have a negative coordinate because _____

_____

_____

SCORE ⓪ ① ②

0 = Incorrect or No Response
1 = Partial Response
2 = Complete and Accurate

TOPIC 3

TOPIC 2

TOPIC 1

Multiply Positive Numbers by Negative Numbers

> WORKED EXAMPLE   > TRY IT   > GUIDED LEARNING

WORKED EXAMPLE

Find the product of 3 and −1.5.

STEP 1 Connect the equation to multiplication.

x	y = 3x	y
2	3•2	6
1	3•1	3
0	3•0	0

STEP 2 Use the pattern to find the products.

x	y = 3x	y
2	3•2	6
1	3•1	3
0	3•0	0
−1	3•(−1)	−3
−2	3•(−2)	−6

(−3 pattern between each row)

STEP 3 Reason to find the product.

When one factor is positive and the other factor is _negative_, the product is _negative_.

$$3•(-1.5) = -4.5$$

STEP 4 Plot to verify the solution.

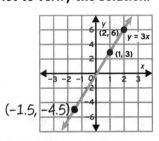

TRY IT

1 Use the table and graph to find the product of 1 and −2.

x	y = 1x	y
2		2
1		1
0		0
−1		
−2		

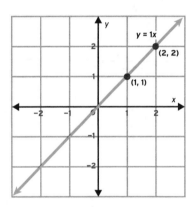

$$1•(-2) = \underline{\hspace{1cm}}$$

GUIDED LEARNING

2 Find the product of 0.5 and −3.

STEP 1 Connect the equation to multiplication.

x	y = 0.5x	y
2		1
1		0.5
0		0
−1		
−2		

STEP 2 Use the pattern to find the products.

STEP 3 Reason to find the product.

When one factor is positive and the other factor is _____, the product is _____.

$$0.5•(-3) = \underline{\hspace{1cm}}$$

STEP 4 Plot to verify the solution.

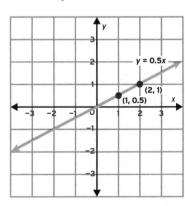

BLOCK 7

factor (n) the number you multiply to find a product

product (n) the result of multiplication

> **PRACTICE**

3

Find the product of 1.5 and −4.

STEP 1 Connect the equation to multiplication.

x	y = 1.5x	y
2		3
1		1.5
0		0
−1		
−2		

STEP 2 Use the pattern to find the products.

STEP 3 Reason to find the product.

$1.5 \cdot (-4) =$ _____

STEP 4 Plot to verify the solution.

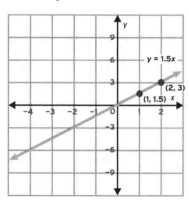

4

Find the product of 2.5 and −3.

STEP 1 Connect the equation to multiplication.

x	y = 2.5x	y
2		5
1		2.5
0		0
−1		
−2		

STEP 2 Use the pattern to find the products.

STEP 3 Reason to find the product.

$2.5 \cdot (-3) =$ _____

STEP 4 Plot to verify the solution.

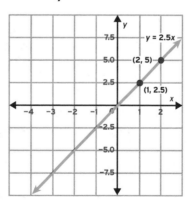

> **Solve the problem.**

Find the product of 4 and −2.5.

x	y = 4x	y
2		8
1		4
0		0
−1		
−2		

$4 \cdot (-2.5) =$ _____

> **Is the product of −4 and 2.5 equal to the product of 4 and −2.5? Explain.**

The product of −4 and 2.5 is / is not equal to the product of 4 and −2.5 because _____

_____

_____

_____

_____

_____

_____

TOPIC 3

TOPIC 2

TOPIC 1

SCORE ⓪ ① ②

0 = Incorrect or No Response
1 = Partial Response
2 = Complete and Accurate

LESSON 4
CONCEPT

Find Solutions in the Coordinate Plane

> WORKED EXAMPLE

> TRY IT

> GUIDED LEARNING

Generate solutions to the equation $y = \frac{1}{2}x$.

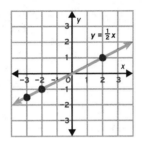

STEP 1 Find the solution in the first quadrant.

x	$y = \frac{1}{2}x$	y
3	$\frac{1}{2} \cdot 3$	$1\frac{1}{2}$
2	$\frac{1}{2} \cdot 2$	1

__(2, 1)__ is a solution to $y = \frac{1}{2}x$.

STEP 2 Find solutions in the third quadrant.

x	$y = \frac{1}{2}x$	y
3	$\frac{1}{2} \cdot 3$	$1\frac{1}{2}$
2	$\frac{1}{2} \cdot 2$	1
0	$\frac{1}{2} \cdot 0$	0
-2	$\frac{1}{2} \cdot (-2)$	-1
-3	$\frac{1}{2} \cdot (-3)$	$-1\frac{1}{2}$

__(-2, -1)__ is a solution to $y = \frac{1}{2}x$.

__$(-3, -1\frac{1}{2})$__ is a solution to $y = \frac{1}{2}x$.

STEP 3 Find another solution.

(-8, __-4__) is a solution to $y = \frac{1}{2}x$.

---

1 Generate solutions to the equation $y = 2x$.

x	y = 2x	y
3	2·3	6
2	2·2	
0	2·0	0
-2	2·(-2)	
-3		

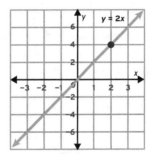

(2, ____) is a solution to $y = 2x$.

(-2, ____) is a solution to $y = 2x$.

(-3, ____) is a solution to $y = 2x$.

(-2.5, ____) is a solution to $y = 2x$.

---

2 Generate solutions to the equation $y = 0.25x$.

x	y = 0.25x	y
3	0.25·3	0.75
2		
0	0.25·0	0
-2		
-3		

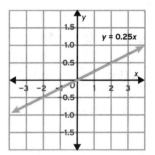

STEP 1 Find the solution in the first quadrant.

_____ is a solution to $y = 0.25x$.

STEP 2 Find solutions in the third quadrant.

_____ is a solution to $y = 0.25x$.

_____ is a solution to $y = 0.25x$.

STEP 3 Find another solution.

(-4.8, ____) is a solution to $y = 0.25x$.

---

factor *(n)* the number you multiply to find a product

product *(n)* the result of multiplication

> **PRACTICE**

3

Generate solutions to the equation $y = 0.1x$.

x	y = 0.1x	y
3	0.1•3	0.3
2		
0	0.1•0	0
−2		
−3		

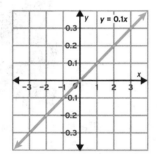

STEP 1 Find the solution in the first quadrant.

_____ is a solution to $y = 0.1x$.

STEP 2 Find solutions in the third quadrant.

_____ is a solution to $y = 0.1x$.

_____ is a solution to $y = 0.1x$.

STEP 3 Find another solution.

(−15, _____) is a solution to $y = 0.1x$.

4

Generate solutions to the equation $y = 3x$.

x	y = 3x	y
3	3•3	9
2		
0	3•0	0
−2		
−3		

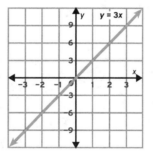

STEP 1 Find the solution in the first quadrant.

_____ is a solution to $y = 3x$.

STEP 2 Find solutions in the third quadrant.

_____ is a solution to $y = 3x$.

_____ is a solution to $y = 3x$.

STEP 3 Find another solution.

(−4.2, _____) is a solution to $y = 3x$.

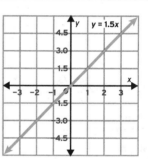

> **Solve the problem.**

Generate solutions to the equation $y = 1.5x$.

x	y = 1.5x	y
3	1.5•3	4.5
2		
0	1.5•0	0
−2		
−3		

> **James says (−4, 6) is a solution to the equation. How would you respond?**

I would say that (−4, 6) is / is not a solution because

_____

_____

_____

_____

SCORE ⓪ ① ②   0 = Incorrect or No Response
1 = Partial Response
2 = Complete and Accurate

TOPIC 3

TOPIC 2

TOPIC 1

First, I'll think about the product I want to capture. If the product is negative, I know I need both a positive factor and a negative factor.

RULES
Multiplication Station (Level 1)

What You Need
- *mSpace* pages 102–105
- Sticky notes

What to Know
- Players take turns.
- A player may place a sticky note on top of another.
- Players check each other's calculations.

How to Win
- The first player to get four in a row horizontally, vertically, or diagonally is the winner.

BLOCK 7

> HOW TO PLAY

STEP 1 **Player A places sticky notes on two factors.**

-36	-24	-18	72	-54
-20	48	-45	-6	-40
-72	40	FREE	-42	90
-21	-8	32	-10	-63
-30	-14	16	24	-56

-9 [ ] -6 -5 -4 -3 -1
1 2 4 6 [ ] 9 10

STEP 2 **Player A records the equation and marks an X on the product.**

-36	-24	-18	72	-54
-20	48	-45	-6	-40
-72	40	FREE	-42	90
-21	-8	32	-10	-63
-30	-14	16	24	✗

-9 [ ] -6 -5 -4 -3 -1
1 2 4 6 [ ] 9 10

PLAYER A	
TURN	EQUATIONS
1	$(-7) \cdot 8 = -56$
2	

STEP 3 **Player B moves one sticky note to a new factor.**

-36	-24	-18	72	-54
-20	48	-45	-6	-40
-72	40	FREE	-42	90
-21	-8	32	-10	-63
-30	-14	16	24	✗

-9 -7 -6 [ ] -4 -3 -1
1 2 4 6 [ ] 9 10

STEP 4 **Player B records the equation and marks an O on the product.**

-36	-24	-18	72	-54
-20	48	-45	-6	(-40)
-72	40	FREE	-42	90
-21	-8	32	-10	-63
-30	-14	16	24	✗

-9 -7 -6 [ ] -4 -3 -1
1 2 4 6 [ ] 9 10

PLAYER B	
TURN	EQUATIONS
1	$(-5) \cdot 8 = -40$
2	

RECORDING SHEET
Multiplication Station
(Level 1)

> Players record their equations and check their partner's work.

-36	-24	-18	72	-54
-20	48	-45	-6	-40
-72	40	FREE	-42	90
-21	-8	32	-10	-63
-30	-14	16	24	-56

-9	-7	-6	-5	-4	-3	-1

1	2	4	6	8	9	10

PLAYER A

TURN	EQUATIONS
1	
2	
3	
4	
5	
6	
7	
8	
9	
10	

PLAYER B

TURN	EQUATIONS
1	
2	
3	
4	
5	
6	
7	
8	
9	
10	

BLOCK 7 > TOPIC 1
LESSON 5
GAME

RECORDING SHEET
Multiplication Station
(Level 1)

> Players record their equations and check their partner's work.

-36	-24	-18	72	-54
-20	48	-45	-6	-40
-72	40	**FREE**	-42	90
-21	-8	32	-10	-63
-30	-14	16	24	-56

-9	-7	-6	-5	-4	-3	-1

1	2	4	6	8	9	10

PLAYER A

TURN	EQUATIONS
1	
2	
3	
4	
5	
6	
7	
8	
9	
10	

PLAYER B

TURN	EQUATIONS
1	
2	
3	
4	
5	
6	
7	
8	
9	
10	

MUSIC DATA ANALYSTS collect data and analyze trends in the music industry. They may look at revenue from CD sales and MP3 downloads to help inform how well an album is doing.

The graph shows earnings from the sale of CDs and MP3 downloads from the release of a rock band's new album.

> **What is the total sales earned by the album in the first six months?**

_____

_____

_____

_____

> **The table shows the expenses paid by the band. Complete the table to find the total cost of producing the album.**

Expense	Rate	Number / Quantity	Expression	Cost
Video	$60 per hr	25 hours	(−60) • 25	−$1500
Recording Studio	$100 per hr	30 hours		
Design	$40 per hr	22 hours		
Manufacturing	$2.50 per CD	10,000		
			Total Cost	

> **Based on the costs and earnings from sales, how much profit did the album earn in the first six months?**

_____

_____

> **Answer this question.**

You need a product of −36 to win. The sticky notes are on the factors 8 and −7. Is it possible to win? Explain.

_____ • _____ = _____

It is / is not possible to win the game because _____

_____

_____

_____

_____

TOPIC 2

> **You want to block your opponent from getting the product −36. Which factors should you avoid placing sticky notes on?**

I would avoid placing sticky notes on _____

because _____

_____

_____

TOPIC 1

SCORE ⓪ ① ②   0 = Incorrect or No Response
1 = Partial Response
2 = Complete and Accurate

BLOCK 7

LESSON 1

Tell Me All That You Can

> About (1, 2), (–1, 2), (–1, –2), and (1, –2).

• _____

• _____

• _____

• _____

> **If connected, what shape would the points form?**

The points would form a _____

because _____

_____

_____

_____

_____

LESSON 2

Brain Teaser

> **Use the graph to solve the riddle.**

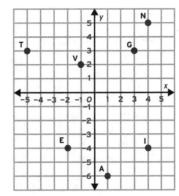

What word describes a direction of moving down or to the left?

___ ___ ___ ___ ___ ___ ___ ___
(4, 5) (–2, –4) (3, 3) (1, –6) (–5, 3)(4, –4) (–1, 2) (–2, –4)

> **How did you start solving this puzzle?**

I started solving this puzzle by

_____

_____

_____

_____

_____

LESSON 3

Find the Pattern

> **Find the change between point A and point B. Then, plot point C using this pattern of change.**

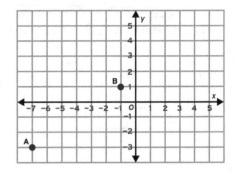

Slope $\left(\frac{\text{change in } y}{\text{change in } x}\right)$: _____

> **Kay says it is not possible to plot another point that fits this pattern. Do you disagree or agree?**

I agree / disagree with Kay

because _____

_____

_____

_____

_____

LESSON 4

Build It

> **Use the numbers to create the coordinates for points A and B when the change in y is –4 and the change in x is 3.**

| –3 | 1 | –2 | 3 | –1 | 2 |

Point A: _____

Point B: _____

> **What do you notice about the x-coordinates of point A and point B?**

I notice that the x-coordinate of

_____

_____

_____

_____

_____

LESSON 5

Brain Arcade

> **Draw a chain of 3 slices of toast in order from least to greatest.**

- _____

- _____

- _____

> **Find a chain of five toasts in order from least to greatest.**

- _____

- _____

- _____

- _____

- _____

In this Topic, you learned how to find slope in all four quadrants.

Which point do I start from to find the slope of the line?

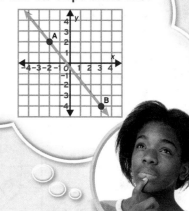

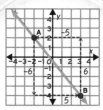

The slope of the line from:

- Point A to B is $\dfrac{-6}{5}$.

- Point B to A is $\dfrac{6}{-5}$.

Both $\dfrac{-6}{5}$ and $\dfrac{6}{-5}$ are equivalent to $-\dfrac{6}{5}$, so I can start from either point A or point B.

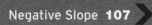

LESSON 1
PROBLEM SOLVING

Create Reflections in the Coordinate Plane

> **WORKED EXAMPLE**

Kemar is creating a symmetrical design for a kite. The graph shows the first half of the design. Create and describe the reflection over the *x*-axis.

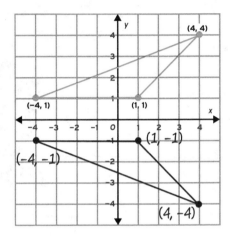

STEP 1 Analyze the problem.

STEP 2 Plot the reflection points.

STEP 3 Draw the reflection.

STEP 4 Describe the pattern.

In a reflection over the __X__-axis, the __X__-coordinates stay the same and the __Y__-coordinates are the additive inverses of the original coordinates.

> **TRY IT**

1 Darren created a figure and its reflection in a lake. The top figure is the original, and the bottom figure is the reflected image. The *x*-axis represents the surface of the lake. Complete the table.

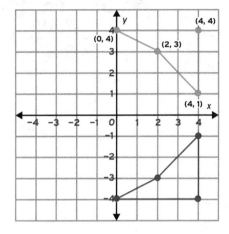

Original	Reflection
(0, 4)	
(4, 4)	
(4, 1)	
(2, 3)	

> **GUIDED LEARNING**

2 Tamara is designing a symmetrical album cover. The graph shows the first half of the cover. Create and describe the reflection over the *y*-axis.

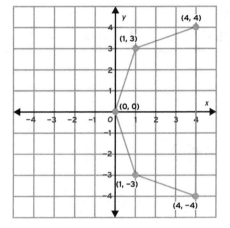

STEP 1 Analyze the problem.

STEP 2 Plot the reflection points.

STEP 3 Draw the reflection.

STEP 4 Describe the pattern.

In a reflection over the ____-axis, the ____-coordinates stay the same and the ____-coordinates are the additive inverses of the original coordinates.

> **PRACTICE**

3 Mario is creating a symmetrical design for an amusement park blueprint. The graph shows the first half of the design. Create and describe the reflection over the *y*-axis.

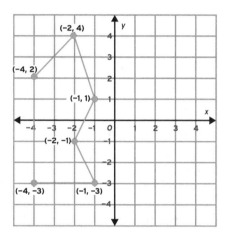

4 Stacey is creating a symmetrical design for a model car grille. The graph shows the first half of the design. Create and describe the reflection over the *x*-axis.

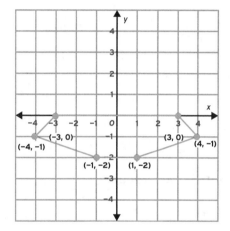

EXIT
Ticket

BLOCK
7

TOPIC 3

TOPIC 2

TOPIC 1

> **Find the error and fix it.**

Antonio reflected a figure over the *x*-axis.

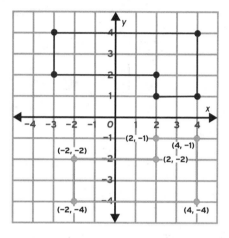

> **Explain the error and how you fixed it.**

_____

_____

_____

_____

_____

SCORE ⓪ ① ②   0 = Incorrect or No Response
1 = Partial Response
2 = Complete and Accurate

Find Change Between Coordinates

> WORKED EXAMPLE

> TRY IT

> GUIDED LEARNING

Find the horizontal and vertical change between point A and point B.

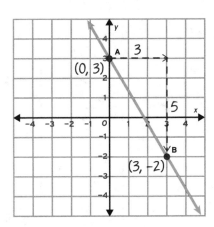

STEP 1 Find the coordinates of the points.

STEP 2 Label the change in each direction.

STEP 3 Find the change in one variable.

The _horizontal_ change is _positive_.

Change in _x_ : _3 − 0 = +3_

STEP 4 Find the change in the other variable.

The _vertical_ change is _negative_.

Change in _y_ : _(−2) − 3 = −5_

---

1 Find the horizontal and vertical change between point A and point B.

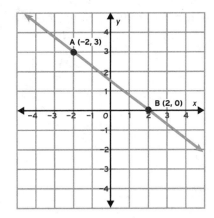

Horizontal change: _____

Vertical change: _____

---

2 Find the horizontal and vertical change between point A and point B.

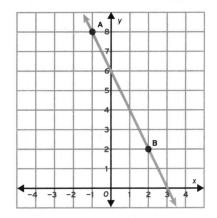

STEP 1 Find the coordinates of the points.

STEP 2 Label the change in each direction.

STEP 3 Find the change in one variable.

The _____ change is

_____.

Change in _____: _____

STEP 4 Find the change in the other variable.

The _____ change is

_____.

Change in _____: _____

BLOCK 7

> PRACTICE

3

Find the horizontal and vertical change between point E and point F.

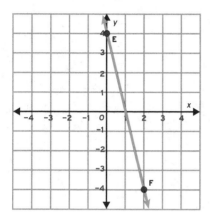

Change in _____: _____

Change in _____: _____

4

Find the horizontal and vertical change between point A and point B.

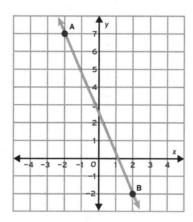

Change in _____: _____

Change in _____: _____

5

Find the horizontal and vertical change between point C and point D.

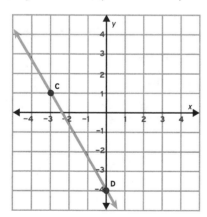

Change in _____: _____

Change in _____: _____

6

Find the horizontal and vertical change between point K and point L.

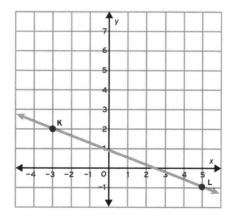

Change in _____: _____

Change in _____: _____

EXIT Ticket

BLOCK **7**

> **Find and fix the errors.**

Find the horizontal and vertical change between points P and Q.

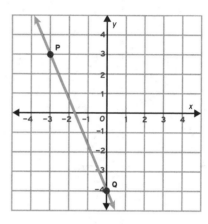

Change in *x*: $0 - (-3) = -3$

Change in *y*: $3 - (-4) = 7$

> **What was the error made and how did you correct it?**

The error this person made was _____

_____

_____

_____

_____

_____

_____

SCORE ⓪ ① ②

0 = Incorrect or No Response
1 = Partial Response
2 = Complete and Accurate

TOPIC 3

TOPIC 2

TOPIC 1

Negative Slope **111** ❯

Identify Slope in Four Quadrants

Find the slope of the line.

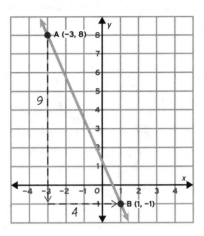

STEP 1 Label the change in each direction.

STEP 2 Find the change in one variable.

The change in y is _negative_.

Change in y: $(-1) - 8 = -9$

STEP 3 Find the change in the other variable.

The change in x is _positive_.

Change in x: $1 - (-3) = 4$

STEP 4 Express the slope as a fraction.

Slope $\left(\frac{\text{change in } y}{\text{change in } x}\right)$: $\frac{-9}{4}$ or $-\frac{9}{4}$

1

Find the slope of the line.

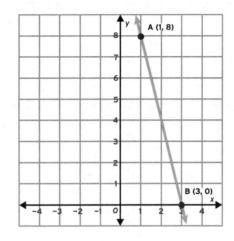

Slope $\left(\frac{\text{change in } y}{\text{change in } x}\right)$: _____

2

Find the slope of the line.

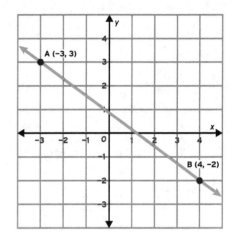

STEP 1 Label the change in each direction.

STEP 2 Find the change in one variable.

The change in ___ is _____.

Change in ___: _____

STEP 3 Find the change in the other variable.

The change in ___ is _____.

Change in ___: _____

STEP 4 Express the slope as a fraction.

Slope $\left(\frac{\text{change in } y}{\text{change in } x}\right)$: _____

factor (n) the number you multiply to find a product

product (n) the result of multiplication

Ticket

7

> PRACTICE

3

Find the slope of the line.

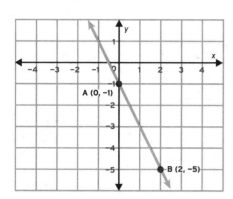

STEP 1 Label the change in each direction.

STEP 2 Find the change in one variable.

The change in ___ is _____.

Change in ___: _____

STEP 3 Find the change in the other variable.

The change in ___ is _____.

Change in ___: _____

STEP 4 Express the slope as a fraction.

Slope $\left(\frac{\text{change in } y}{\text{change in } x}\right)$: _____

4

Find the slope of the line.

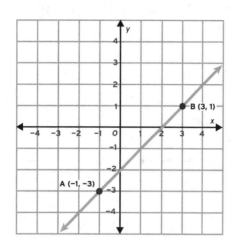

STEP 1 Label the change in each direction.

STEP 2 Find the change in one variable.

The change in ___ is _____.

Change in ___: _____

STEP 3 Find the change in the other variable.

The change in ___ is _____.

Change in ___: _____

STEP 4 Express the slope as a fraction.

Slope $\left(\frac{\text{change in } y}{\text{change in } x}\right)$: _____

> **Solve the problem.**

Find the slope of the line.

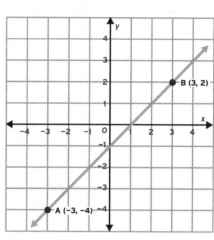

Change in ___: _____

Change in ___: _____

Slope $\left(\frac{\text{change in } y}{\text{change in } x}\right)$: _____

> **How can you use arrows to find slope?**

I can use arrows to _____

_____

_____

_____

TOPIC 3

TOPIC 2

TOPIC 1

SCORE ⓪ ① ②

| 0 = Incorrect or No Response |
| 1 = Partial Response |
| 2 = Complete and Accurate |

Use Slope to Show Fraction Equivalence

What is the slope of the line from point A to point B and from point B to point A?

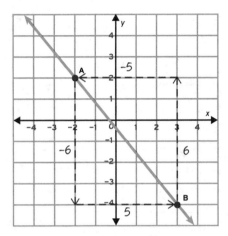

STEP 1 Describe the slope of the line.

The slope of the line is _negative_.

STEP 2 Find the slope from point A to point B.

Slope $\left(\frac{\text{change in } y}{\text{change in } x}\right)$: $\frac{-6}{5}$

STEP 3 Find the slope from point B to point A.

Slope $\left(\frac{\text{change in } y}{\text{change in } x}\right)$: $\frac{6}{-5}$

STEP 4 Reason about the values of the fractions.

The fractions $\frac{-6}{5}$ and $\frac{6}{-5}$

are equivalent to $\frac{-6}{5}$.

1

What is the slope of the line from point A to point B and from point B to point A?

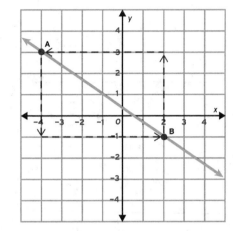

Slope of point A to B $\left(\frac{\text{change in } y}{\text{change in } x}\right)$: _____

Slope of point B to A $\left(\frac{\text{change in } y}{\text{change in } x}\right)$: _____

2

What is the slope of the line from point A to point B and from point B to point A?

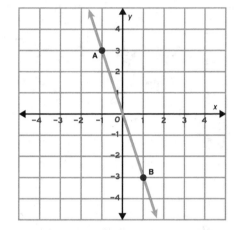

STEP 1 Describe the slope of the line.

The slope of the line is _____.

STEP 2 Find the slope from point A to point B.

Slope $\left(\frac{\text{change in } y}{\text{change in } x}\right)$: _____

STEP 3 Find the slope from point B to point A.

Slope $\left(\frac{\text{change in } y}{\text{change in } x}\right)$: _____

STEP 4 Reason about the values of the fractions.

The fractions _____ and _____

are equivalent to _____.

> PRACTICE

3 What is the slope of the line from point A to point B and from point B to point A?

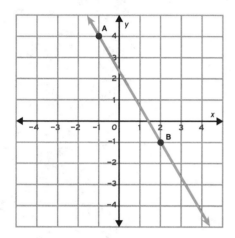

STEP 1 Describe the slope of the line.

The slope of the line is _____.

STEP 2 Find the slope from point A to point B.

Slope $\left(\frac{\text{change in } y}{\text{change in } x}\right)$: _____

STEP 3 Find the slope from point B to point A.

Slope $\left(\frac{\text{change in } y}{\text{change in } x}\right)$: _____

STEP 4 Reason about the values of the fractions.

The fractions _____ and _____

are equivalent to _____.

4 What is the slope of the line from point A to point B and from point B to point A?

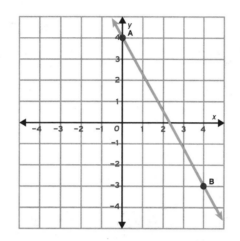

STEP 1 Describe the slope of the line.

The slope of the line is _____.

STEP 2 Find the slope from point A to point B.

Slope $\left(\frac{\text{change in } y}{\text{change in } x}\right)$: _____

STEP 3 Find the slope from point B to point A.

Slope $\left(\frac{\text{change in } y}{\text{change in } x}\right)$: _____

STEP 4 Reason about the values of the fractions.

The fractions _____ and _____

are equivalent to _____.

EXIT Ticket

BLOCK **7**

TOPIC 3

> Solve the problem.

What is the slope of the line from point A to point B and from point B to point A?

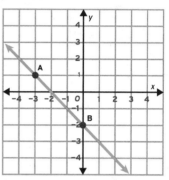

Slope $\left(\frac{\text{change in } y}{\text{change in } x}\right)$ = _____

Slope $\left(\frac{\text{change in } y}{\text{change in } x}\right)$ = _____

> Compare the two fractions naming the slope of the line. How are they similar and different?

The two slopes are similar because _____

_____

The two slopes are different because _____

_____

_____

_____

TOPIC 2

TOPIC 1

SCORE ⓪ ① ②
0 = Incorrect or No Response
1 = Partial Response
2 = Complete and Accurate

I think about ways to multiply mentally. To find $\frac{3}{4}$ of a number, I find $\frac{1}{4}$ of the number and multiply it 3 times.

RULES
Multiplication Station (Level 2)

What You Need
- *mSpace* pages 116–119
- Sticky notes

What to Know
- Players take turns.
- Players may place one sticky note on top of another.
- Players check each other's calculations.

How to Win
- The first player to get four in a row horizontally, vertically, or diagonally is the winner.

> HOW TO PLAY

BLOCK 7

STEP 1 **Player A places sticky notes on two factors.**

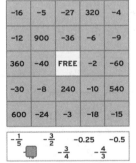

STEP 2 **Player A records the equation and marks an X on the product.**

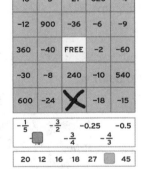

PLAYER A	
TURN	**EQUATIONS**
1	$\left(-\frac{1}{10}\right) \times 30 = -3$

STEP 3 **Player B moves only one sticky note to a new factor.**

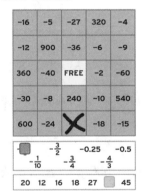

STEP 4 **Player B records the equation and marks an O on the product.**

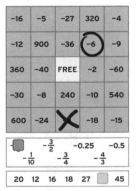

PLAYER B	
TURN	**EQUATIONS**
1	$\left(-\frac{1}{5}\right) \times 30 = -6$

-16	-5	-27	320	-4
-12	900	-36	-6	-9
360	-40	FREE	-2	-60
-30	-8	240	-10	540
600	-24	-3	-18	-15

$$-\frac{1}{5} \qquad -\frac{3}{2} \qquad -0.25 \qquad -0.5$$
$$-\frac{1}{10} \qquad -\frac{3}{4} \qquad -\frac{4}{3}$$

| 20 | 12 | 16 | 18 | 27 | 30 | 45 |

PLAYER A

TURN	EQUATIONS
1	
2	
3	
4	
5	
6	
7	
8	
9	
10	

PLAYER B

TURN	EQUATIONS
1	
2	
3	
4	
5	
6	
7	
8	
9	
10	

BLOCK 7 > TOPIC 2
LESSON 5
GAME

RECORDING SHEET
Multiplication Station
(Level 2)

> Record your equations, and check your partner's work.

-16	-5	-27	320	-4
-12	900	-36	-6	-9
360	-40	FREE	-2	-60
-30	-8	240	-10	540
600	-24	-3	-18	-15

$$-\frac{1}{5} \qquad -\frac{3}{2} \qquad -0.25 \qquad -0.5$$
$$-\frac{1}{10} \qquad -\frac{3}{4} \qquad -\frac{4}{3}$$

20	12	16	18	27	30	45

PLAYER A

TURN	EQUATIONS
1	
2	
3	
4	
5	
6	
7	
8	
9	
10	

PLAYER B

TURN	EQUATIONS
1	
2	
3	
4	
5	
6	
7	
8	
9	
10	

SPORTS PHOTOGRAPHERS capture the exciting moments of a sports event, such as when they take a shot of the winning point. They may need to think about the amount of light available and adjust the opening in their camera lens, called the aperture.

The graph shows the amount of illuminating light, measured in the unit lux, on a partly cloudy day.

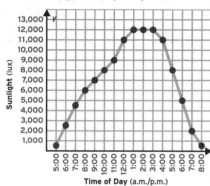

A sports photographer may use this graph to decide the size of the camera's lens opening, or aperture.

- For a greater amount of light, a smaller aperture is needed.

- For a lesser amount of light, a larger aperture is needed.

› **The diagram shows different aperture sizes on a camera.**

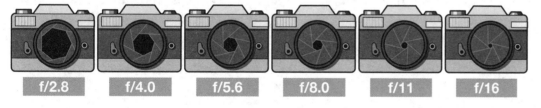

| f/2.8 | f/4.0 | f/5.6 | f/8.0 | f/11 | f/16 |

Which aperture should a sports photographer use at a 12:00 p.m. (noon) soccer game? Explain.

_____

_____

Which aperture should the sports photographer use at a 6:00 p.m. game?

_____

_____

EXIT Ticket

› **Solve the problem.**

Match each product to the correct pair of factors.

$-\frac{1}{4} \cdot 36$		-15
$-0.2 \cdot 50$		-24
$-\frac{3}{2} \cdot 16$		-6
$-0.75 \cdot 20$		-9
$-\frac{1}{5} \cdot 30$		-10

› **Choose one of the examples and explain how you can find the product mentally.**

I can find the product of

_____ mentally by

_____

_____

_____

_____

_____

SCORE ⓪ ① ②

0 = Incorrect or No Response
1 = Partial Response
2 = Complete and Accurate

Who's Right?

> Three students give different descriptions of the point (3, 2) reflected over the *x*-axis.

Andrew	Luisa	Xavier
The reflection will be the point (3, −2).	The reflection will be in the second quadrant.	The reflection will be the point (−3, 2).

Who's right? _____

> What is the pattern between the number of sides and lines of symmetry in a figure?

The number of sides is _____ the number of lines of symmetry because _____

_____

_____

_____

_____

Find the Pattern

> Find the pattern to complete the missing values in the table.

x	y
1.5	
	2
0.5	
0	0
	−1

> What is the value of *y* when *x* = −2? Explain.

When *x* = −2, the *y*-value is _____ because _____

_____

_____

_____

_____

_____

_____

Which Does Not Belong?

> These expressions have something in common. Circle the expression that does not belong.

4 • 2	(−2) • 4	$\frac{1}{3}$ • (−6)
(−8) • (−1)	16 • $\frac{1}{2}$	(−4) • (−2)

> What is another expression that does not belong? Explain your reasoning.

Another expression that does not belong is _____ because _____

_____

_____

_____

_____

_____

LESSON 4

Number Strings

> Insert parentheses to make the equations true.

- $2 \times 3 + 4 - 2 + 5 \times 2 = 18$

- $2 \times 3 + 4 - 2 + 5 \times 2 = 22$

> How did you use the order of operations to make the equations true?

I used the order of operations by

_____

_____

_____

_____

_____

_____

LESSON 5

Brain Teaser

> Solve this puzzle when a square represents a product and two circles are the factors.

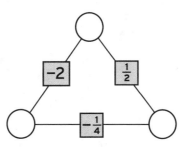

> What steps did you take to solve this problem?

I began solving this problem by

_____ Then, I _____

_____

_____

_____

_____

_____

_____

_____

> In this Topic, you learned how to multiply and divide negative numbers.

How do I find the quotient of 20 and −2.5?

I'll write 20 ÷ (−2.5) as a multiplication equation because multiplication and division are inverse operations.

_____ × (−2.5) = 20

I know that the sign of the missing factor is negative because the product is positive. So, 20 ÷ (−2.5) is −8.

> WORKED EXAMPLE

Reflect the figure over the origin and describe the pattern.

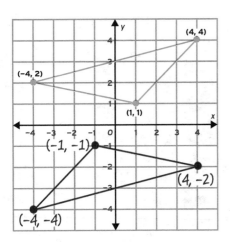

STEP 1 Analyze the problem.

STEP 2 Plot the reflection points.

STEP 3 Draw the reflection.

STEP 4 Describe the pattern.

The coordinates of a reflection over the origin are the *additive inverses* of the originals.

> TRY IT

1 Reflect the figure over the vertical axis. Then, reflect a third image over the horizontal axis.

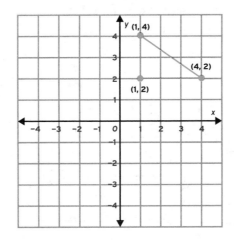

> GUIDED LEARNING

2 Reflect the figure over the origin and describe the pattern.

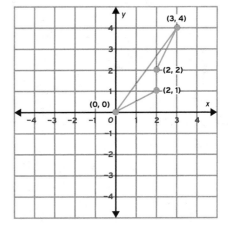

STEP 1 Analyze the problem.

STEP 2 Plot the reflection points.

STEP 3 Draw the reflection.

STEP 4 Describe the pattern.

The coordinates of a reflection over the origin are the _____ of the originals.

> PRACTICE

3 Reflect the image over the origin and describe the pattern.

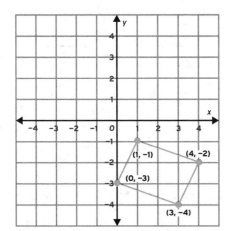

The coordinates of a reflection over the origin are the _____ of the originals.

4 Reflect the image over the origin and describe the pattern.

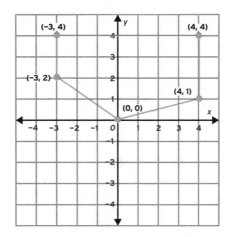

The coordinates of a reflection over the origin are the _____ of the originals.

EXIT Ticket

BLOCK **7**

> **Answer these questions.**

The reflection of the point (4, 4) over the y-axis is _____.

The reflection of the point (4, 4) over the x-axis is _____.

The reflection of the point (4, 4) over the origin is _____.

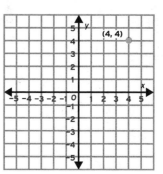

TOPIC 3

TOPIC 2

In the coordinate plane, reflecting a point over the origin is the same as reflecting a point over both axes.

TOPIC 1

SCORE ⓪ ① ② | 0 = Incorrect or No Response
1 = Partial Response
2 = Complete and Accurate

Multiply Rational Numbers

> **WORKED EXAMPLE**

> **TRY IT**

> **GUIDED LEARNING**

BLOCK 7

WORKED EXAMPLE

Find the product of −2 and −2.1.

STEP 1 Multiply to find solutions with positive x-values.

x	y = −2x	y
2	(−2)•2	−4
1	(−2)•1	−2

STEP 2 Use the pattern to find the products.

x	y = −2x	y
0	(−2)•0	0
−1	(−2)•(−1)	2
−2	(−2)•(−2)	4
−3	(−2)•(−3)	6

+2
+2
+2

STEP 3 Describe the rule.

When both factors are negative, the product is _positive_ .

When multiplying a negative and positive factor, the product is a _negative_ .

STEP 4 Apply the rule to find the product.

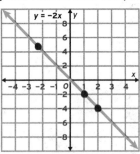

(−2)•(−2.1) = ___4.2___

TRY IT

1

Use the graph and equation to find y when x = −2.5.

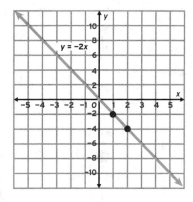

y = −2x

y = _____

GUIDED LEARNING

2

Find the product of −3 and −2.2.

STEP 1 Multiply to find solutions with positive x-values.

x	y = −3x	y
2		
1		
0	(−3)•0	0
−1		
−2		
−3		

STEP 2 Use the pattern to find the products.

STEP 3 Describe the rule.

When both factors are negative, the product is _____.

When multiplying a negative and positive factor, the product is a _____.

STEP 4 Apply the rule to find the product.

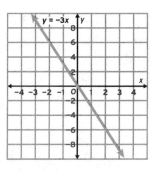

(−3)•(−2.2) = _____

> PRACTICE

3 Find the product of −5 and −26.

$(-5) \cdot (-26) =$ _____

4 Find the product of −12 and 0.2.

$(-12) \cdot 0.2 =$ _____

5 Find the product of −1.5 and 2.4.

$(-1.5) \cdot 2.4 =$ _____

6 Find the product of −2.1 and −3.

$(-2.1) \cdot (-3) =$ _____

7 Find the product of −18 and $-\frac{1}{2}$.

$(-18) \cdot (-\frac{1}{2}) =$ _____

8 Find the product of $-\frac{3}{4}$ and −24.

$(-\frac{3}{4}) \cdot (-24) =$ _____

9 Find the product of 1, 2, and −3.

$1 \cdot 2 \cdot (-3) =$ _____

10 Find the product of −1, −5, and −8.

$(-1) \cdot (-5) \cdot (-8) =$ _____

EXIT Ticket

BLOCK 7

> **Find and fix the error.**

Find the product of −2 and −4.5.

$$(-2) \cdot (-4.5) = \underline{-0.9}$$

TOPIC 3

> **What was the mistake this person made?**

The mistake this person made was _____

_____

_____

_____

TOPIC 2

> **What would be the sign of the product if another factor is added to the problem: $(-2) \cdot (-4.5) \cdot (-1)$?**

I can find the product by_____

TOPIC 1

_____

_____

_____

_____

SCORE ⓪ ① ②

0 = Incorrect or No Response
1 = Partial Response
2 = Complete and Accurate

Multiply Negative Numbers to Find Solutions

> WORKED EXAMPLE

Evaluate $y = -\frac{2}{3}x - 1$ when $x = -3$ to find the solution.

STEP 1 Substitute the value of x.

$$y = -\frac{2}{3}x - 1$$

$$y = \left(-\frac{2}{3}\right) \cdot (-3) - 1$$

STEP 2 Multiply to simplify the expression.

$$y = \frac{6}{3} - 1$$

STEP 3 Find the value of y.

$$y = 2 - 1$$
$$y = 1$$

STEP 4 Express the solution and plot to verify.

__(−3, 1)__ is a solution to $y = -\frac{2}{3}x - 1$.

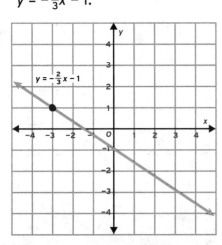

> TRY IT

1 Find the solution to $y = \frac{1}{3}x - 3$ when $x = -3$.

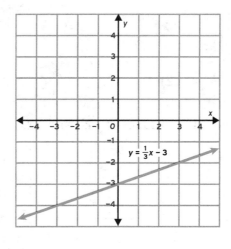

_____ is a solution to $y = \frac{1}{3}x - 3$.

> GUIDED LEARNING

2 Evaluate $y = -\frac{2}{5}x - 3$ when $x = -5$ to find the solution.

STEP 1 Substitute the value of x.

$$y = -\frac{2}{5}x - 3$$

STEP 2 Multiply to simplify the expression.

STEP 3 Find the value of y.

STEP 4 Express the solution and plot to verify.

_____ is a solution to $y = -\frac{2}{5}x - 3$.

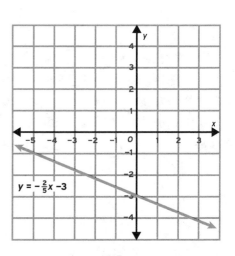

BLOCK 7

order of operations *(n)* the sequence in which operations are performed to evaluate an expression

3 Evaluate $y = -\frac{3}{2}x - 1$ when $x = -2$ to find the solution.

$$y = -\frac{3}{2}x - 1$$

_____ is a solution to $y = -\frac{3}{2}x - 1$.

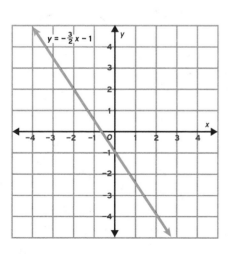

4 Evaluate $y = -\frac{3}{5}x - 2$ when $x = -5$ to find the solution.

$$y = -\frac{3}{5}x - 2$$

_____ is a solution to $y = -\frac{3}{5}x - 2$.

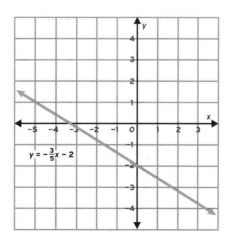

EXIT Ticket

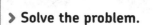

> **Solve the problem.**

Evaluate $y = -\frac{1}{2}x - 3$ when $x = -4$ to find the solution.

$$y = -\frac{1}{2}x - 3$$

_____ is a solution to the equation.

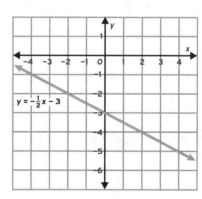

> **How does the graph help you verify the solution?**

The graph helps me verify the solution by _____

_____

_____

SCORE ⓪ ① ②

0 = Incorrect or No Response
1 = Partial Response
2 = Complete and Accurate

BLOCK **7**

TOPIC 3

TOPIC 2

TOPIC 1

Divide Negative Numbers to Find Solutions

> **WORKED EXAMPLE**

What is $10 \div (-2.5)$?

STEP 1 Write the related multiplication equation.

Multiplication equation:

$(-2.5) \cdot \underline{\hspace{1cm}} = 10$

STEP 2 Find the sign of the other factor.

Sign of missing factor:

negative

STEP 3 Find the quotient in the division equation.

$10 \div (-2.5) = \underline{-4}$

STEP 4 Multiply to verify the solution.

$(-2.5) \cdot (-4) = 10$

$10 = 10$

> **TRY IT**

1

What is $(-3) \div 1.5$?

$1.5 \cdot \underline{\hspace{1cm}} = -3$

$(-3) \div 1.5 = \underline{\hspace{1cm}}$

> **GUIDED LEARNING**

2

What is $(-7.5) \div (-5)$?

STEP 1 Write the related multiplication equation.

Multiplication equation:

STEP 2 Find the sign of the other factor.

Sign of missing factor:

_____

STEP 3 Find the quotient in the division equation.

$-7.5 \div (-5) = \underline{\hspace{1cm}}$

STEP 4 Multiply to verify the solution.

> **PRACTICE**

3

What is $3.5 \div (-2)$?

$3.5 \div (-2) =$ _____

4

What is $4.5 \div (-1.5)$?

$4.5 \div (-1.5) =$ _____

5

What is $(-5.2) \div (-4)$?

$(-5.2) \div (-4) =$ _____

6

What is $(-15) \div 2.5$?

$(-15) \div 2.5 =$ _____

7

What is $(-9.6) \div (-3)$?

$(-9.6) \div (-3) =$ _____

8

What is $(-24.8) \div (-4)$?

$(-24.8) \div (-4) =$ _____

EXIT Ticket

BLOCK **7**

> **Solve the problem.**

What is $5.25 \div (-1.75)$?

Multiplication equation:

Sign of the missing factor:

_____

$5.25 \div (-1.75) =$ _____

TOPIC 3

TOPIC 2

> **What steps did you take to solve the problem?**

The steps I took to solve the problem were _____

_____

_____

_____

_____

_____

_____

_____

_____

_____

TOPIC 1

SCORE ⓪ ① ②

0 = Incorrect or No Response
1 = Partial Response
2 = Complete and Accurate

Operations With Negative Numbers **129**

LESSON 5
PROBLEM SOLVING

Solve Puzzles With Rational Numbers

ANCHOR VIDEO CONNECTION

As the Anchor Video shows, developments in math and science can impact the way we entertain ourselves.

> You are writing an app for a math game. You need to write an equation so the app can assess answers to this puzzle.

The puzzle involves the Multiplicative Identity Property and multiplicative inverses.

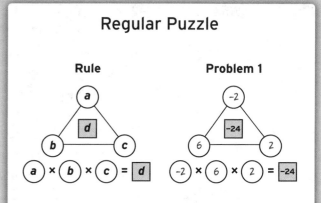

Regular Puzzle

A CREATE

Create two puzzles whose products are −1.

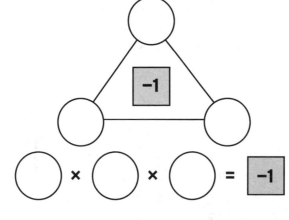

Puzzle 1

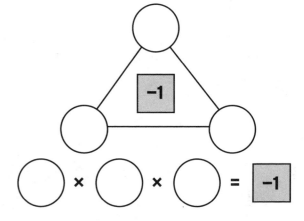

Puzzle 2

BLOCK 7

BIG IDEA 1 **Symbolic representations** help to clearly communicate mathematical ideas.

BIG IDEA 2 **Different types of numbers** are necessary to solve a range of problems.

B PREDICT

Describe the pattern in all solutions. You may write an expression describing one variable in terms of the others.

_____

_____

_____

_____

_____

_____

C EXPLAIN

Ned says this puzzle can't be solved without multiplicative inverses and negative numbers. Do you agree or disagree? Explain your reasoning.

_____

_____

_____

_____

_____

_____

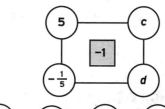

EXIT
Ticket

> **Solve the problem.**

Sandra is creating a similar puzzle for a newspaper. Complete the puzzle.

$$5 \times \left(-\frac{1}{5}\right) \times \bigcirc \times \bigcirc = \boxed{-1}$$

> **Describe values of c and d that solve the puzzle.**

The values of c and d must be

_____

_____

_____

We need fractions and negative numbers to solve certain types of problems.

BLOCK **7**

TOPIC 3

TOPIC 2

TOPIC 1

SCORE ⓪ ① ②

0 = Incorrect or No Response
1 = Partial Response
2 = Complete and Accurate

> **YOUR JOB**
> Film Producer

> **YOUR TASK**
> Determine which format to distribute your films in—DVDs or online streaming.

 ANCHOR VIDEO CONNECTION

As the Anchor Video shows, technological advances will lead to different forms of entertainment. This will also affect sales trends in the entertainment industry.

Compare With Negative Slope

> **You are a producer in the film industry. Your task is to use data to determine whether your films should continue to be distributed on DVD, or whether you should change to online streaming only.**

A EXPLORE

The table shows the data on your company's film distribution for the past 2 years since 2012. Assuming these trends stay constant, write an equation and graph a line for the annual profits for both DVDs and online streaming.

Time (yr)	Profit (millions of $)	
	DVDs	**Online Streaming**
−2	200	50
−1	150	100
0	100	150

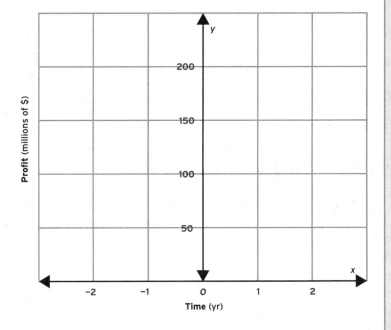

y represents the _____

x represents the _____

Annual DVD profits:

$y =$ _____

Annual streaming profits:

$y =$ _____

1. This year is year 0. Based on this trend, in how many years from now will DVD profits be $0?

DVD profits will be $0 in _____ years.

2. When DVD profits reach $0, how much will streaming profits be?

Streaming profits will be $_____ million when DVD profits are $0.

EXPLAIN In how many years should your company stop distributing DVDs? Explain your reasoning.

_____

_____

_____

REFLECT Niki says you should have stopped distributing DVDs 2 years ago. Do you agree or disagree? Why?

_____

_____

_____

Evaluate

> Rate how well you and your partner understood and completed each part of the performance task.

Ranking Scale			
None	Limited	Partial	Thorough
0	1	2	3

A Completed the graph and equations.

| Me | 0 | 1 | 2 | 3 |
| Partner | 0 | 1 | 2 | 3 |

B Accurately used your equations to solve the problems.

| Me | 0 | 1 | 2 | 3 |
| Partner | 0 | 1 | 2 | 3 |

C Answered each question thoughtfully.

| Me | 0 | 1 | 2 | 3 |
| Partner | 0 | 1 | 2 | 3 |

EXTEND

In how many years will the total profit of DVDs and online streaming combined be greater than they were 2 years ago? Explain your reasoning.

_____

_____

_____

_____

_____

_____

BLOCK 7 MINDSET STRATEGY

Reflect on Developing Grit
Congratulations! You've completed Block 7 of *MATH 180*.

From Rock 'n' Roll to Rocket Science

Adam Steltzner helped land a rover on Mars. Yet in high school, he struggled in math. "I convinced my folks, my teachers, and myself that I was a terrible student." He joined a rock band rather than going to college.

Developing Grit

One night while driving home from a gig, he pulled over because he noticed the constellation Orion in the sky. That night made him curious about the stars. By focusing on something he cared about, Steltzner developed **grit**, which is **sustained effort toward a long-term goal**. People with grit "stick with it" when things get tough.

Living the Dream

Steltzner went to community college and took elementary algebra. Only 7 years later, he landed a job at NASA's Jet Propulsion Laboratory. Because he was gritty, Steltzner is now living his dream.

> ❯ **What goals or interests do you have that could give you the grit to keep at it in math?**
>
> _____
>
> _____
>
> _____
>
> _____
>
> _____

Adam Steltzner,
NASA Engineer

❝ *At first it was very, very hard. I got mediocre grades, but things eventually improved. It turns out that with the correct mindset, I kind of rocked at math.* ❞

—Adam Steltzner, at IDEAS event

How to "Get Grit"

Grit is sticking with a task even when it gets difficult. Here are some ways to strengthen your grit.

1 Develop a growth mindset.

Fixed mindset:
There are things I can't learn. Why try? It doesn't matter.

Growth mindset:
I can grow my intelligence. My effort helps me improve.

2 Monitor your self-talk.

Instead of this:
This just isn't for me. I will never catch up.

Say this:
I can get better at learning and learn a lot from hard things.

3 Keep your eyes on the goal.

Visualize success:
Think about what success feels like.

Find your meaning:
Connect math to something you care about.

Developing Grit in *MATH 180*

> Make a goal for yourself in the Learn Zone.

My goal for the Learn Zone is...

> Thinking of your goal above, use the How to "Get Grit" strategy above to fill in the chart below.

1 DEVELOP A GROWTH MINDSET

2 MONITOR YOUR SELF-TALK

3 KEEP YOUR EYES ON THE GOAL

Fixed mindset	Growth mindset	Instead of this	Say this	Visualize success	Find your meaning
				When I achieve this goal, I will...	I can connect the math to something I care about by...

VOCABULARY

- exponent
- function
- input
- nonlinear
- output
- quadratic function
- square
- square root

Hack Masters

When is hacking helpful?

Computer hacking isn't always a crime. In this Anchor Video, see how one team of researchers hacks into computers and other personal devices to make them more secure.

Math in Information Technology

In this Block, you will see how functions are used in information technology.

Programmers

use **functions** to build applications. For example, one function might **input** your date of birth and **output** your age.

Ethical Hackers

help prevent data theft and fraud. They look for a computer **function** that allows them to break into computer networks before real criminals can.

Cryptologists

are people whose job is to create codes. Many methods of doing this require calculating **squares** and **square roots** of numbers.

Digital Forensic Scientists

are people who investigate computer-related, or cyber, crimes. They use **square roots** to help trace the origin of a digital image.

Engineers

measure distance to ensure radio antennae are close to transmitting towers. A radio signal's strength is related to the **square** of the distance.

BLOCK 8

Block Preview

> Read the Career Explorations on *mSpace* page 135. Which career interests you the most? Why?

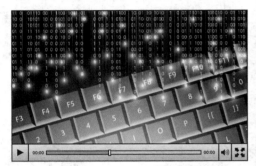

The career that interests me the most is _____

because _____

_____

> How do ethical hackers use math?

Ethical hackers use math by

_____

_____

_____

Missing Numbers

> Fill in numbers to make the equation true.

$$\underline{\quad} \cdot 8 + \underline{\quad} = 36$$

> How did you begin solving this problem?

I began solving this problem by ___

_____

_____

_____

Which Does Not Belong?

> Circle the input-output pair that does not belong.

Input: 10
Output: −5

Input: 4
Output: −2

Input: −8
Output: 4

Input: −9
Output: 3

Input: 7
Output: −3.5

> How can you change the pair you circled so that it does belong?

I can change _____

_____

_____

_____

LESSON 4

Brain Arcade

> Circle the flowerpot that makes the equation true.

$(-7) \cdot (-0.6) = $ _____

> Which corn would you use to complete the equation
> $-7 \times$ _____ $= -5.6$?

I would use the corn labeled _____

because _____

_____

_____

LESSON 5

Tell Me All That You Can

> List as many things as you can about this graph.

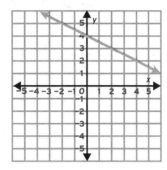

- _____
- _____
- _____
- _____

_____

_____

> What is the equation of the line?

The equation of the line is _____

_____

_____

_____

_____

_____

> In this Topic, you learned to graph linear functions and represent linear functions with equations.

How do inputs and outputs relate to ordered pairs?

Input (x)	Output (y)	(x, y)
0	−2	(0, −2)
2	4	(2, 4)

The input represents the x-coordinate and the output represents the y-coordinate.

ANCHOR VIDEO CONNECTION

As the Anchor Video shows, both linear and nonlinear patterns can be found in all forms of information technology.

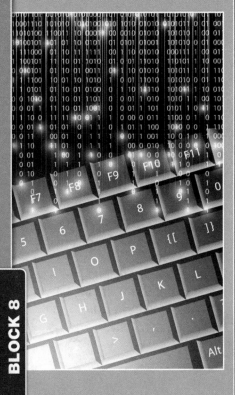

Create Security Codes

> You are an ethical hacker. You have been hired by a company to test its security system.

Each employee is given an ID number. The ID number is tested through two functions.

- The first function takes the ID number as the input and finds the sum of the digits. This sum is the output.

- The second function takes the sum as the input and finds the product of the digits. This product is the output.

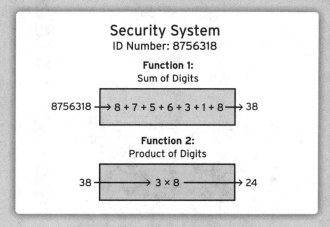

Security System
ID Number: 8756318

Function 1:
Sum of Digits

$8756318 \rightarrow 8+7+5+6+3+1+8 \rightarrow 38$

Function 2:
Product of Digits

$38 \rightarrow 3 \times 8 \rightarrow 24$

A CREATE

For extra security, all valid ID numbers must have a final output that is a multiple of 3. Create an ID number that will pass the company's security system.

BIG IDEA 1 Unlike nonlinear functions, linear functions have a **constant rate of change**.

BIG IDEA 2 Functions can be described with patterns or with **mathematical rules for inputs to find outputs**.

B PREDICT

Omar says that 2867301 is a valid ID number. Will Omar's ID number pass the company's security system?

_____

_____

_____

_____

_____

_____

C EXPLAIN

Is the extra security measure a third function? Explain why or why not.

_____

_____

_____

_____

EXIT Ticket

BLOCK 8

TOPIC 3

> *Select all that apply.*

Find the possible functions for the ID number 2868927.

☐ The sum of the digits is 42.

☐ The product of the digits of the sum is 18.

☐ The ID number is valid.

☐ The ID number is a multiple of 3.

TOPIC 2

TOPIC 1

A linear relationship can be proportional, but nonlinear relationships are not proportional.

SCORE ⓪ ① ②

0 = Incorrect or No Response
1 = Partial Response
2 = Complete and Accurate

> WORKED EXAMPLE

> TRY IT

> GUIDED LEARNING

Graph the linear function $y = 3x - 2$. Use the inputs $x = 0$ and $x = 2$.

STEP 1 Reason about the function.

The slope is ___3___, so the function is (increasing) / decreasing.

STEP 2 Use the first input to evaluate the function.

Input (x)	y = 3x − 2	Output (y)	(x, y)
0	(3)(0) − 2 0 − 2 = −2	−2	(0, −2)

STEP 3 Use the second input to evaluate the function.

Input (x)	y = 3x − 2	Output (y)	(x, y)
0	(3)(0) − 2 0 − 2 = −2	−2	(0, −2)
2	(3)(2) − 2 6 − 2 = 4	4	(2, 4)

STEP 4 Plot the input-output pairs to graph the function.

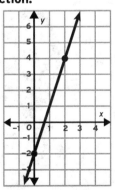

1 Complete the table using the equation $y = x + 1$.

x	y = x + 1	y	(x, y)
−2	y = (−2) + 1	−1	(−2, −1)
−1			
0			
1			
2			

2 Graph the linear function $y = -2x + 6$. Use the inputs $x = 0$ and $x = 3$.

STEP 1 Reason about the function.

The slope is _____, so the function is increasing / decreasing.

STEP 2 Use the first input to evaluate the function.

Input (x)	y = −2x + 6	Output (y)	(x, y)
0			
3			

STEP 3 Use the second input to evaluate the function.

STEP 4 Plot the input-output pairs to graph the function.

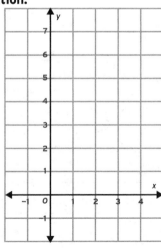

BLOCK 8

input *(n)* a value we substitute for a variable in a function to determine a corresponding unique output

output *(n)* the result of applying a function rule to an input

> PRACTICE

3

Graph the linear function $y = -1x + 5$.
Use the inputs $x = 0$ and $x = 6$.

The slope is _____, so the function is increasing / decreasing.

Input (x)	$y = -1x + 5$	Output (y)	(x, y)
0			
6			

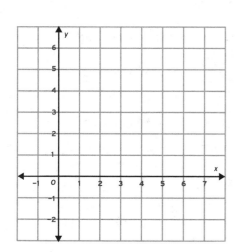

4

Graph the linear function $y = -\frac{1}{2}x + 4$.
Use the inputs $x = -2$ and $x = 8$.

The slope is _____, so the function is increasing / decreasing.

Input (x)	$y = -\frac{1}{2}x + 4$	Output (y)	(x, y)
-2			
8			

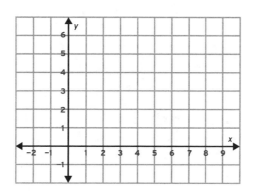

> **Find and fix the error in the table.**

TOPIC 3

Input (x)	$y = -3x - 7$	Output (y)	(x, y)
-3	$(-3)(-3) - 7$ $9 - 7 = 2$	2	(-3, 2)
5	$(-3)(5) - 7$ $-15 - 7 = -22$	-22	(-22, 5)

> **Explain the error and how you fixed it.**

TOPIC 2

_____

_____

_____

_____

The input of a function is the *x*-value. The output of a function is the *y*-value.

TOPIC 1

SCORE ⓪ ① ②

0 = Incorrect or No Response
1 = Partial Response
2 = Complete and Accurate

Graph a Line From an Equation

Graph the line $y = 3x + 1$.

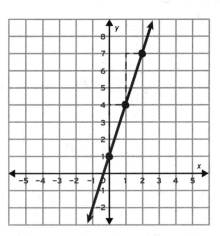

STEP 1 Plot and identify the y-intercept.

y-intercept: $(0, 1)$

STEP 2 Express the slope as a fraction.

Slope: $\frac{3}{1} = \frac{6}{2}$

STEP 3 Use the slope to plot another point.

Points: $(1, 4)$
$(2, 7)$

STEP 4 Choose a point to verify the line.

Point: $(1, 4)$

$y = 3x + 1$

$4 = 3(1) + 1$
$4 = 3 + 1$
$4 = 4$

1 Graph the line $y = 3x - 2$ given the y-intercept.

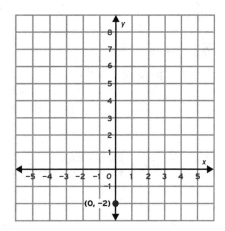

2 Graph the line $y = -\frac{2}{3}x + 5$.

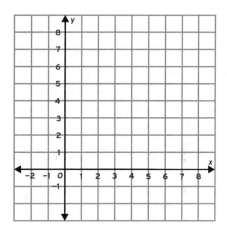

STEP 1 Plot and identify the y-intercept.

y-intercept:

STEP 2 Express the slope as a fraction.

Slope:

STEP 3 Use the slope to plot another point.

Points:

STEP 4 Choose a point to verify the line.

Point:

$y = -\frac{2}{3}x + 5$

> PRACTICE

3 Graph the line $y = -1x + 8$.

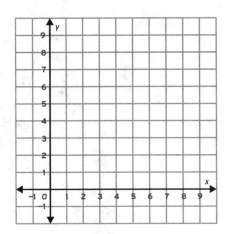

STEP 1 **Plot and identify the y-intercept.**

y-intercept:

STEP 2 **Express the slope as a fraction.**

Slope:

STEP 3 **Use the slope to plot another point.**

Points:

STEP 4 **Choose a point to verify the line.**

Point:

$y = -1x + 8$

4 Graph the line $y = \frac{3}{4}x - 5$.

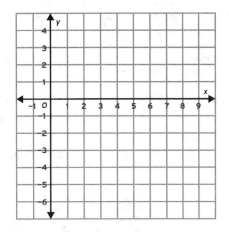

STEP 1 **Plot and identify the y-intercept.**

y-intercept:

STEP 2 **Express the slope as a fraction.**

Slope:

STEP 3 **Use the slope to plot another point.**

Points:

STEP 4 **Choose a point to verify the line.**

Point:

$y = \frac{3}{4}x - 5$

EXIT Ticket

> **Solve the problem.**

Graph the line $y = -2x + 4$.

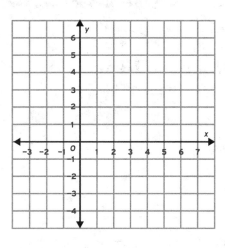

y-intercept:

Slope:

Points:

$y = -2x + 4$

BLOCK 8

TOPIC 3

TOPIC 2

TOPIC 1

SCORE ⓪ ① ②

0 = Incorrect or No Response
1 = Partial Response
2 = Complete and Accurate

I can start with the equations in which I can use mental math to find the output.

RULES
Function Junction (Level 1)

What You Need
- *mSpace* pages 144–147

What to Know
- Players take turns and decide who is X and O.
- Players check each other's calculations.

How to Win
- The first player to get three in a row wins the round.
- The player that wins the most rounds out of three games is the winner.

> HOW TO PLAY

BLOCK 8

STEP 1 Choose an equation and an input.

$-\frac{3}{2}$	$\frac{1}{2}$	4
6	0	−2
−10	−5	−8

PLAYER A			
EQUATIONS	INPUT	SUBSTITUTE	OUTPUT
$y = x - 1$	5		

STEP 2 Find the output.

$-\frac{3}{2}$	$\frac{1}{2}$	4
6	0	−2
−10	−5	−8

PLAYER A			
EQUATIONS	INPUT	SUBSTITUTE	OUTPUT
$y = x - 1$	5	$y = 5 - 1$	4

STEP 3 Mark the output on the game board.

$-\frac{3}{2}$	$\frac{1}{2}$	✗
6	0	−2
−10	−5	−8

PLAYER A			
EQUATIONS	INPUT	SUBSTITUTE	OUTPUT
$y = x - 1$	5	$y = 5 - 1$	4

RECORDING SHEET
Function Junction
(Level 1)

› Players record their equations and check their partner's work.

ROUND 1

$-\dfrac{3}{2}$	$\dfrac{1}{2}$	4
6	0	-2
-3	2	-8

INPUTS:

-4	-3	-2	-1	0	1	2	3	4

EQUATIONS:

$y = 2x$

$y = 3x + 1$

$y = x - 1$

$y = \dfrac{1}{2}x$

$y = \dfrac{3}{2}x$

$y = -2x$

$y = x + 1$

$y = -\dfrac{1}{2}x$

$y = \dfrac{3}{2}x - 2$

PLAYER A

EQUATION	INPUT	SUBSTITUTE	OUTPUT

PLAYER B

EQUATION	INPUT	SUBSTITUTE	OUTPUT

ROUND 2

-5	$\dfrac{3}{2}$	-1
-6	1	-4
3	$\dfrac{1}{4}$	$-\dfrac{1}{2}$

INPUTS:

-4	-3	-2	-1	$\dfrac{1}{2}$	1	2	3	4

EQUATIONS:

$y = 2x$

$y = 3x + 1$

$y = x - 1$

$y = \dfrac{1}{2}x$

$y = \dfrac{3}{2}x$

$y = -2x$

$y = -x + 1$

$y = -\dfrac{1}{2}x$

$y = \dfrac{3}{2}x - 2$

PLAYER A

EQUATION	INPUT	SUBSTITUTE	OUTPUT

PLAYER B

EQUATION	INPUT	SUBSTITUTE	OUTPUT

BLOCK 8 > TOPIC 1
LESSON 4
GAME

RECORDING SHEET
Function Junction
(Level 1)

> Players record their equations and check their partner's work.

ROUND 3

2	$-\frac{3}{2}$	−5
−1	0	$-\frac{1}{2}$
−3	3	1

INPUTS:

| $-\frac{1}{2}$ | $\frac{1}{2}$ | 1 | 2 | 3 | 4 | −1 | −2 | −4 | −3 |

EQUATIONS:

$y = 3x$

$y = 2x - 4$

$y = x - 3$

$y = -x$

$y = -2x + 1$

$y = -x - 1$

$y = -3x$

$y = -\frac{1}{2}x + \frac{1}{2}$

$y = 4x + 3$

$y = x + \frac{1}{2}$

PLAYER A

EQUATION	INPUT	SUBSTITUTE	OUTPUT

PLAYER B

EQUATION	INPUT	SUBSTITUTE	OUTPUT

ROUND 4

$-\frac{3}{2}$	$\frac{1}{2}$	4
6	1	−2
−3	2	−8

INPUTS:

| $-\frac{1}{2}$ | $\frac{1}{2}$ | 1 | 2 | 3 | 4 | −1 | −2 | −4 | −3 |

EQUATIONS:

$y = 3x$

$y = 2x - 4$

$y = x - 3$

$y = -x$

$y = -2x + 1$

$y = -x - 1$

$y = -3x$

$y = -\frac{1}{2}x + \frac{1}{2}$

$y = 4x - 3$

$y = x + \frac{1}{2}$

PLAYER A

EQUATION	INPUT	SUBSTITUTE	OUTPUT

PLAYER B

EQUATION	INPUT	SUBSTITUTE	OUTPUT

DIGITAL FORENSIC SCIENTISTS help law enforcement collect, measure, and analyze evidence from crime scenes. They may retrieve information from computers or prove whether items are real or forged.

An unknown painting has been retrieved after an art gallery reported it stolen. A digital forensic scientist creates tables to compare the unknown painting to an original painting.

ORIGINAL PAINTING

Square Inches	Number of Strokes
2	8
5	14
10	24
25	54

UNKNOWN PAINTING

Square Inches	Number of Strokes
4	15
9	35
20	79
30	119

> **What are the functions for both paintings?**

Original Painting: _____

Unknown Painting: _____

> **Is the unknown painting the real painting or a forgery duplicated by a copycat artist? Explain.**

_____

_____

_____

EXIT Ticket

BLOCK 8 — TOPIC 3 — TOPIC 2 — TOPIC 1

> **Solve the problem.**

What is the correct input for the equation $y = -3x - 3$ when the output is 0?

INPUTS:

| −1 | 0 | 1 | 2 | 3 |

$$y = -3x - 3$$

When the output is 0, the input is _____.

> **How did you solve this problem?**

I solved this problem by _____

_____

_____

_____

_____

SCORE ⓪ ① ②

| 0 = Incorrect or No Response |
| 1 = Partial Response |
| 2 = Complete and Accurate |

Represent a Line With an Equation

> WORKED EXAMPLE   > TRY IT   > GUIDED LEARNING

WORKED EXAMPLE

Write the equation of the line, and verify that the point (1, −1) is a solution.

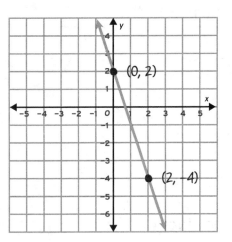

STEP 1 Plot and identify the *y*-intercept.

$b = \underline{\quad 2 \quad}$

STEP 2 Plot a point on the line and find the slope.

$\dfrac{\text{change in } y}{\text{change in } x} : -\dfrac{6}{2}$

$m = \underline{\quad -3 \quad}$

STEP 3 Represent the line with an equation.

Equation: $\underline{\quad y = -3x + 2 \quad}$

STEP 4 Verify that the point represents a solution.

$-1 = -3(1) + 2$
$-1 = -3 + 2$
$-1 = -1$

TRY IT

1 Write the equation of the line.

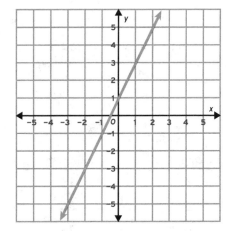

y-intercept: _____

$b = \underline{\qquad}$

$m = \underline{\qquad}$

$y = mx + b$

Equation: _____

GUIDED LEARNING

2 Write the equation of the line, and verify that the point (−1, 0) is a solution.

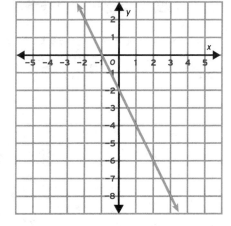

STEP 1 Plot and identify the *y*-intercept.

$b = \underline{\qquad}$

STEP 2 Plot a point on the line and find the slope.

$\dfrac{\text{change in } y}{\text{change in } x} :$

$m = \underline{\qquad}$

STEP 3 Represent the line with an equation.

Equation: _____

STEP 4 Verify that the point represents a solution.

equation *(n)* a mathematical sentence that states that two quantities are equal

point *(n)* a location or position

> PRACTICE

3

Write the equation of the line, and verify that the point (2, −3) is a solution.

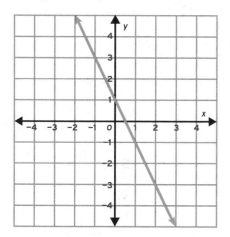

STEP 1 Plot and identify the *y*-intercept.

$b =$ _____

STEP 2 Plot a point on the line and find the slope.

$\dfrac{\text{change in } y}{\text{change in } x}:$

$m =$ _____

STEP 3 Represent the line with an equation.

Equation: _____

STEP 4 Verify that the point represents a solution.

4

Write the equation of the line, and verify that the point (−4, 0) is a solution.

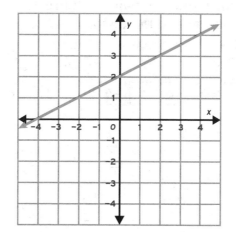

STEP 1 Plot and identify the *y*-intercept.

$b =$ _____

STEP 2 Plot a point on the line and find the slope.

$\dfrac{\text{change in } y}{\text{change in } x}:$

$m =$ _____

STEP 3 Represent the line with an equation.

Equation: _____

STEP 4 Verify that the point represents a solution.

> Solve the problem.

Write the equation of the line, and verify that the point (1, 2) is a solution.

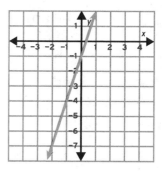

$b =$ _____

$\dfrac{\text{change in } y}{\text{change in } x}:$

$m =$ _____

Equation: _____

> How did you use the line to find the slope?

To find the slope, I _____

_____

_____

_____

SCORE ⓪ ① ②   **0** = Incorrect or No Response
1 = Partial Response
2 = Complete and Accurate

BLOCK **8**

TOPIC 3

TOPIC 2

TOPIC 1

LESSON 1

Brain Teaser

> Solve this riddle.

- If my graph is shifted up 3 units, the equation of the new line is $y = 3x + 5$.

- If my graph is shifted down 2 units, the equation of the new line is $y = 3x$.

What is the equation? _____

> **What do all of these lines have in common?**

These lines all share _____

_____

_____

_____

_____

LESSON 2

Build It

> **Choose inputs and outputs to make ordered pairs that are solutions to the linear function $y = 14x - 5$.**

| 9 | 0 | -33 | 1 | -5 | -1 | -19 | -2 |

- _____
- _____
- _____
- _____

> **How do you know you have found all the ordered pairs?**

I know I have found all the ordered pairs because _____

_____

_____

_____

LESSON 3

Missing Numbers

> **Place the numbers below to make the equations true.**

| -5 | -2 | 9 |

$$40 = (-9)(\quad) - 5$$

$$-3 = (-2)(6) + (\quad)$$

$$-2 = (\quad)(3) + 4$$

> **How did you solve the first equation?**

To solve the first equation, I

_____

_____

_____

_____

LESSON 4

Who's Right?

> Owen and Jen found the slope between points A and B.

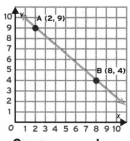

A (2, 9)

B (8, 4)

Owen	Jen
$m = -\dfrac{5}{6}$	$m = -\dfrac{6}{5}$

Who's right? _____

> How did you begin solving this problem?

First, I _____

_____ Then, I _____

_____

_____

_____

_____

LESSON 5

Brain Arcade

> Select a number on the turntable that makes the equation true.

SCORE 250

TIMER 1:51

$-\frac{7}{10}$ $\frac{7}{10}$ 1.4   2

$-5 \times y = 3.5$

POWER BEAT

$-5 \times$ _____ $= 3.5$

> How did you solve the equation?

I solved the equation by _____

_____

_____

_____

_____

> In this Topic, you learned how to solve linear equations and identify nonlinear relationships.

What is the difference between a linear relationship and a nonlinear relationship?

A linear relationship has a constant rate of change, while a nonlinear relationship does not.

Linear

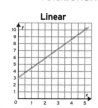

Nonlinear

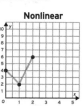

Represent Functions in Multiple Forms

> WORKED EXAMPLE

> TRY IT

> GUIDED LEARNING

Kim, an event planner, is digitally recreating a restaurant event. The tables increase in size. How many chairs will be around table 6?

STEP 1 Extend the sequence.

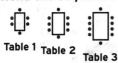

Table 1   Table 2   Table 3

STEP 2 Identify the pattern.

Table (n)	Number of Chairs (c)
1	6
2	8
3	10
4	12
5	14

STEP 3 Represent the function with an equation.
Equation: $c = dn + z$
$d = 2$
$(1, 6)$
$6 = 2(1) + z$
$6 = 2 + z$
$6 - 2 = 2 - 2 + z$
$4 = z$ or $z = 4$

STEP 4 Solve the problem.
$c = 2n + 4$
$c = 2(6) + 4$
$c = 12 + 4$
$c = 16$

There will be __16__ chairs around table 6.

---

1 Xena is using toothpicks to build big squares out of little squares. Based on this pattern, how many little squares will be in square 5?

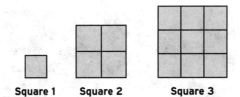

Square 1   Square 2   Square 3

There will be _____ little squares in square 5.

---

2 Elan is creating a path of tiled arches for an animated entrance on his home page. The arches increase in size. How many tiles will Elan need for arch 10?

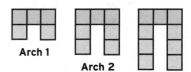

Arch 1

Arch 2

Arch 3

Arch (n)	Number of Tiles (t)
1	5
2	7
3	9
4	
5	

Equation: $t = dn + z$

Elan will need _____ tiles for arch 10.

> PRACTICE

3

Omar, an app developer, is using plastic beads to create necklaces for an accessory app. How many beads will be in necklace 12?

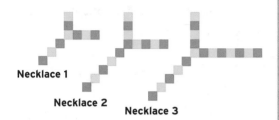

Necklace 1
Necklace 2
Necklace 3

Necklace (*n*)	Number of Beads (*b*)
1	9
2	13
3	17
4	
5	

Equation: *b* = *dn* + *z*

There will be _____ beads in necklace 12.

4

Lola, a digital artist, is creating a sequence of images as part of a dream sequence in an animated film. How many little stars will Lola need for design 20?

Design 1
Design 2
Design 3

Design (*n*)	Number of Little Stars (*s*)
1	6
2	11
3	16
4	
5	

Equation: *s* = *dn* + *z*

Lola will need _____ little stars for design 20.

EXIT Ticket

BLOCK
8

> **Select all that apply.**

Cole is creating a logo by adding red squares in each frame.

Frame 1   Frame 2   Frame 3

☐ *y* = 5*x* + 3 represents the number of red squares (*y*) in frame (*x*).

☐ *y* = 3*x* + 2 represents the number of red squares (*y*) in frame (*x*).

☐ There will be 32 red squares in frame 10.

☐ There will be 53 red squares in frame 10.

I can represent functions in multiple ways using pictures, tables, and equations.

TOPIC 3

TOPIC 2

TOPIC 1

SCORE ⓪ ① ②

0 = Incorrect or No Response
1 = Partial Response
2 = Complete and Accurate

Solve Linear Equations Using Graphs

> WORKED EXAMPLE   > TRY IT   > GUIDED LEARNING

A digital fireworks show contains 450 fireworks. The fireworks are released at a rate of 75 fireworks per minute. After how many minutes will there be 150 fireworks remaining?

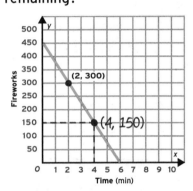

STEP 1 Model the situation with an equation.

$m = \underline{-75}$

$b = \underline{450}$

$y = mx + b$

Equation: $\underline{y = -75x + 450}$

STEP 2 Use the graph to solve the problem.

Solution: $\underline{(4, 150)}$

STEP 3 Substitute to verify the equation.

$150 = (-75)(4) + 450$

$150 = (-300) + 450$

$150 = 150$

There will be 150 fireworks remaining after $\underline{\quad 4 \quad}$ minutes.

---

1 Write the equation of the line. Then, determine the value of x when y = 3.

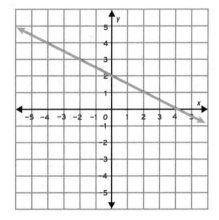

$m = \underline{\hspace{2cm}}$

$b = \underline{\hspace{2cm}}$

$y = mx + b$

Equation: $\underline{\hspace{3cm}}$

Solution: ($\underline{\hspace{1.5cm}}$, 3)

---

2 The graph represents the cost of downloading songs from a music website. Zach has a $5 gift card. If Zach has $3 left on his gift card balance, how many songs has he downloaded?

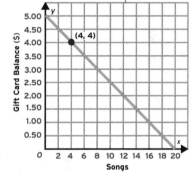

STEP 1 Model the situation with an equation.

$m = \underline{\hspace{2cm}}$

$b = \underline{\hspace{2cm}}$

$y = mx + b$

Equation: $\underline{\hspace{3cm}}$

STEP 2 Use the graph to solve the problem.

Solution: $\underline{\hspace{2.5cm}}$

STEP 3 Substitute to verify the equation.

If Zach has $3 left, he has downloaded $\underline{\hspace{2cm}}$ songs.

EXIT
Ticket

BLOCK
8

> **PRACTICE**

3

Lewis downloaded podcasts. He has already listened to 4 of the podcasts. If he listens to 2 podcasts per day, how many more days will it take him to listen to 14 podcasts altogether?

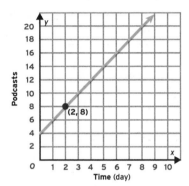

STEP 1 Model the situation with an equation.

m = _____

b = _____

$y = mx + b$

Equation: _____

STEP 2 Use the graph to solve the problem.

Solution: _____

STEP 3 Substitute to verify the equation.

It will take _____ more days for Lewis to listen to 14 podcasts altogether.

4

Mike is sharing a 1-gigabyte movie on his network. His brother, Steve, is downloading the movie at a speed of 0.2 gigabytes per second. How long will it take Steve to download the movie?

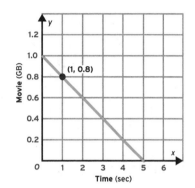

STEP 1 Model the situation with an equation.

m = _____

b = _____

$y = mx + b$

Equation: _____

STEP 2 Use the graph to solve the problem.

Solution: _____

STEP 3 Substitute to verify the equation.

It will take Steve _____ seconds to download the movie.

> **Solve the problem.**

TOPIC 3

After an initial 3 albums, a band releases an album on a music website every two years. How many albums has the band released in 6 years altogether?

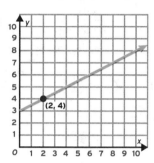

m = _____

b = _____

$y = mx + b$

Equation: _____

Solution: _____

TOPIC 2

TOPIC 1

> **How did you use the graph to solve the problem?**

I used the graph to solve the problem by _____

_____

SCORE ⓪ ① ②

0 = Incorrect or No Response
1 = Partial Response
2 = Complete and Accurate

Solve Two-Step Linear Equations

> **WORKED EXAMPLE**

Mia, a digital forensic scientist, has $500 in her expense account. She spends $75 per week. In how many weeks will Mia's account balance drop to $125?

STEP 1 Model the situation with an equation.

y: amount in the expense account

x: number of weeks

m: -75

b: 500

Equation: $y = -75x + 500$

STEP 2 Substitute the value of y.

$$125 = -75x + 500$$

STEP 3 Find the value that makes the equation true.

$$125 = -75x + 500$$
$$125 - 500 = -75x + 500 - 500$$
$$-375 = -75x$$

STEP 4 Solve the problem.

$$\frac{-375}{-75} = \frac{-75x}{-75}$$
$$\frac{-375}{-75} = x$$
$$5 = x \text{ or } x = 5$$

Mia will have $125 remaining in her expense account in __5__ weeks.

> **TRY IT**

1 Josh, a gaming designer, has a $500 budget. Josh spends $50 on making each game. If he spends $300 on software, how many games can Josh make?

Josh can make _____ games.

> **GUIDED LEARNING**

2 A reality television show begins each season with 50 contestants. At the end of each episode, 3 contestants are eliminated. After how many episodes is the show down to 8 contestants?

STEP 1 Model the situation with an equation.

y: _____

x: _____

m: _____

b: _____

Equation: _____

STEP 2 Substitute the value of y.

STEP 3 Find the value that makes the equation true.

STEP 4 Solve the problem.

The show will have 8 remaining contestants after _____ episodes.

> PRACTICE

3

Shin has $150 in her savings account. Her online banking app charges a $3 fee every month. How many months will it take for Shin to have $123 left in her savings account?

STEP 1 Model the situation with an equation.

y: _____

x: _____

m: _____

b: _____

Equation: _____

STEP 2 Substitute the value of y.

STEP 3 Find the value that makes the equation true.

STEP 4 Solve the problem.

Shin will have $123 in her savings account after _____ months.

4

Grace, a video game designer, has to create a new game with 40 levels. She can complete 2.5 levels per week. How long will it take Grace to complete half the levels?

STEP 1 Model the situation with an equation.

y: _____

x: _____

m: _____

b: _____

Equation: _____

STEP 2 Substitute the value of y.

STEP 3 Find the value that makes the equation true.

STEP 4 Solve the problem.

It will take Grace _____ weeks to complete half the levels.

EXIT Ticket

BLOCK **8**

TOPIC 3

TOPIC 2

TOPIC 1

> **Solve the problem.**

A radio station is giving away 50 concert tickets. Each hour, the station gives away 8 tickets. In how many hours will the radio station be down to the last 2 tickets?

The radio station will be down to the last 2 tickets in _____ hours.

> **Explain how you found your answer.**

I found my answer by _____

_____

_____

_____

_____

_____

_____

SCORE ⓪ ① ②

0 = Incorrect or No Response
1 = Partial Response
2 = Complete and Accurate

> **WORKED EXAMPLE**

Determine if the set of ordered pairs represents a linear function.

Point	x	y	(x, y)
A	0	4	(0, 4)
B	1	2	(1, 2)
C	2	6	(2, 6)

STEP 1 Find the ratio for the first pair of ordered pairs.

Rate of change: $\frac{\text{change in } y}{\text{change in } x}$

A and B: $\frac{2-4}{1-0} = \frac{-2}{1} = -2$

STEP 2 Find the ratio for the other pair of ordered pairs.

B and C: $\frac{6-2}{2-1} = \frac{4}{1} = 4$

STEP 3 Compare the ratios.

The function is linear /(nonlinear)

because the rate of change

is /(is not) constant.

STEP 4 Plot the ordered pairs.

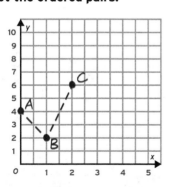

> **TRY IT**

1 Determine if the set of ordered pairs represents a linear function.

Point	x	y	(x, y)
A	1	2	(1, 2)
B	3	6	(3, 6)
C	5	10	(5, 10)

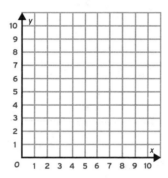

Slope: $\frac{\text{change in } y}{\text{change in } x}$

A and B:

B and C:

A and C:

The function is linear / nonlinear.

> **GUIDED LEARNING**

2 Determine if the set of ordered pairs represents a linear function.

Point	x	y	(x, y)
A	1	1	(1, 1)
B	2	2	(2, 2)
C	3	8	(3, 8)

STEP 1 Find the ratio for the first pair of ordered pairs.

Rate of change: $\frac{\text{change in } y}{\text{change in } x}$

A and B:

STEP 2 Find the ratio for the other pair of ordered pairs.

B and C:

STEP 3 Compare the ratios.

The function is linear / nonlinear

because the rate of change

is / is not constant.

STEP 4 Plot the ordered pairs.

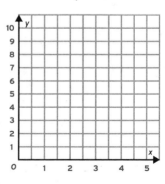

BLOCK 8

nonlinear *(adj)* not forming a line

function *(n)* a set of ordered pairs for which each input has exactly one output

> **PRACTICE**

3

Determine if the set of ordered pairs represents a linear function.

Point	x	y	(x, y)
A	0	8	(0, 8)
B	1	1	(1, 1)
C	2	0	(2, 0)

STEP 1 Find the ratio for the first pair of ordered pairs.

Rate of change: $\frac{\text{change in } y}{\text{change in } x}$

A and B:

STEP 2 Find the ratio for the other pair of ordered pairs.

B and C:

STEP 3 Compare the ratios.

The function is linear / nonlinear

because the rate of change

is / is not constant.

STEP 4 Plot the ordered pairs.

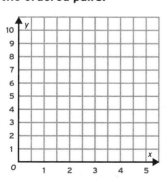

4

Determine if the set of ordered pairs represents a linear function.

Point	x	y	(x, y)
A	0	0	(0, 0)
B	1	4	(1, 4)
C	2	8	(2, 8)

STEP 1 Find the ratio for the first pair of ordered pairs.

Rate of change: $\frac{\text{change in } y}{\text{change in } x}$

A and B:

STEP 2 Find the ratio for the other pair of ordered pairs.

B and C:

STEP 3 Compare the ratios.

The function is linear / nonlinear

because the rate of change

is / is not constant.

STEP 4 Plot the ordered pairs.

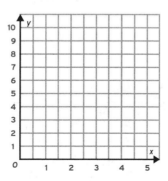

> **Find and fix the error in the table.**

The table represents a linear function. Amy completes the table with the missing ordered pair for point C. Find and fix her error.

Point	x	y	(x, y)
A	0	0	(0, 0)
B	1	3	(1, 3)
C	9	3	(9, 3)

A and B:

B and C:

> In a linear function, the rate of change is constant. In a nonlinear function, the rate of change varies.

SCORE ⓪ ① ②

0 = Incorrect or No Response
1 = Partial Response
2 = Complete and Accurate

Analyzing Functions **159**

For some equations, I can find the input mentally using inverse operations.

RULES

Function Junction (Level 2)

What You Need
- *mSpace* pages 160–163

What to Know
- Players take turns and decide who is X and O.
- Players check each other's calculations.
- Players mark inputs if it appears on the game board.

How to Win
- The first player to mark four connecting squares wins the round.
- The player that wins two out of three rounds is the winner.
- Play a fourth round as a tie breaker.

> HOW TO PLAY

STEP 1 Choose an equation and output.

$\frac{2}{3}$	2	–3	12
4	0	–2	–1
3	6	1	–9
–10	–5	$-\frac{1}{2}$	–4

PLAYER A

EQUATION	OUTPUT	SUBSTITUTE	INPUT
$y = x - 1$	5		

STEP 2 Find the input.

$\frac{2}{3}$	2	–3	12
4	0	–2	–1
3	6	1	–9
–10	–5	$-\frac{1}{2}$	–4

PLAYER A

EQUATION	OUTPUT	SUBSTITUTE	INPUT
$y = x - 1$	5	$5 = x - 1$	6

STEP 3 Mark the input on the game board.

$\frac{2}{3}$	2	–3	12
4	0	–2	–1
3	✗	1	–9
–10	–5	$-\frac{1}{2}$	–4

PLAYER A

EQUATION	OUTPUT	SUBSTITUTE	INPUT
$y = x - 1$	5	$5 = x - 1$	6

RECORDING SHEET
Function Junction
(Level 2)

> Players record their equations and check their partner's work.

ROUND 1

$\frac{2}{3}$	2	-3	12
4	0	-2	-1
3	6	1	-9
-10	-5	$-\frac{1}{2}$	-4

OUTPUTS:

-6	-2	5	1	-4	6	-5	-1	0

EQUATIONS:

$y = -2x$

$y = -x + 2$

$y = x - 1$

$y = -2x - 1$

$y = \frac{1}{2}x - 2$

$y = 3x - 2$

$y = x + 4$

$y = -3x$

$y = \frac{1}{2}x$

ROUND 2

3	-6	2	1
-8	5	-12	-3
4	20	-1	-5
6	-2	8	0

OUTPUTS:

-5	1	-3	2	-1	5	-2	3	0

EQUATIONS:

$y = -1x$

$y = -x + 3$

$y = x - 2$

$y = -x - 4$

$y = \frac{1}{2}x - 5$

$y = 2x - 1$

$y = x + 5$

$y = 5x$

$y = -\frac{1}{4}x$

PLAYER A

EQUATION	OUTPUT	SUBSTITUTE	INPUT

PLAYER B

EQUATION	OUTPUT	SUBSTITUTE	INPUT

PLAYER A

EQUATION	OUTPUT	SUBSTITUTE	INPUT

PLAYER B

EQUATION	OUTPUT	SUBSTITUTE	INPUT

RECORDING SHEET
Function Junction
(Level 2)

> Players record their equations and check their partner's work.

ROUND 3

-1	-9	0	-3
-2	-10	9	-16
12	4	6	8
3	-6	-5	-4

EQUATIONS:

$y = -2x$

$y = -x + 2$

$y = x - 1$

$y = -x - 1$

$y = \frac{1}{2}x - 2$

$y = 2x - 2$

$y = x + 4$

$y = 4x$

$y = -\frac{1}{2}x$

OUTPUTS:

-6 8 12 2 -10 3 -2 -1 0

TIE BREAKER

-1	-9	0	-3
-2	-10	9	-16
12	4	6	8
3	-6	-5	-4

EQUATIONS:

$y = -2x$

$y = -x + 2$

$y = x - 1$

$y = -x - 1$

$y = \frac{1}{2}x - 2$

$y = 2x - 2$

$y = x + 4$

$y = 4x$

$y = -\frac{1}{2}x$

OUTPUTS:

-6 8 12 2 -10 3 -2 -1 0

PLAYER A

EQUATION	OUTPUT	SUBSTITUTE	INPUT

PLAYER B

EQUATION	OUTPUT	SUBSTITUTE	INPUT

PLAYER A

EQUATION	OUTPUT	SUBSTITUTE	INPUT

PLAYER B

EQUATION	OUTPUT	SUBSTITUTE	INPUT

CRYPTOLOGISTS help keep secret information private by creating codes called "encryptions." They may also be asked to crack encryptions to find out top secret information for the government.

Below is a message containing secret information.

"OCZ   NZXMZO   KVNNXJYZ   DN   OCMZZ
ADQZ   JIZ   NZQZI."

> **A key is used to help crack this encrypted message. Finish completing the key. What pattern do you see?**

F		H										
A	B	C	D	E	F	G	H	I	J	K	L	M

	T				Y							E
N	O	P	Q	R	S	T	U	V	W	X	Y	Z

> **Use the key to decode the message.**

" ____ _____ _____
__ _____ _____ ____
_____."

BLOCK 8

TOPIC 3

> **Solve the problem.**

What is the input for the equation when the output is 3?

$$y = -5x - 2$$

The input is _____ in the equation $y = -5x - 2$ when the output is 3.

TOPIC 2

> **How did you solve the problem?**

I solved the problem by _____

_____

_____

_____

_____

_____

TOPIC 1

LESSON 1

Build It

› Find the area of a quadrilateral enclosed by the following points:

A (−6, −2), B (−6, 2), C (2, 2), D (2, −2)

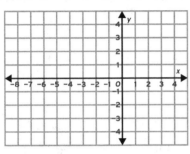

Area: _____

› What was the first step you took in solving this problem?

My first step was to _____

_____

_____

_____

_____

LESSON 2

Tell Me All That You Can

› About the model.

_____

_____

_____

_____

› How does each unit relate to the whole?

Each unit relates to the whole because _____

_____

_____

_____

_____

LESSON 3

Which Does Not Belong?

› These pairs of numbers have something in common. Circle the pair that does not belong.

$\sqrt{16}$ and 4	$(-10)^2$ and 100
6^2 and 36	$\sqrt{25}$ and 5
8^2 and 81	$\sqrt{49}$ and 7

› Which does not belong?

The pair that does not belong is

_____ because _____

_____

_____

_____

_____

LESSON 4

Brain Teaser

> **Solve the riddle.**

- I am an integer.
- I am less than 0.
- My square is 36.
- I am 12 less than my opposite.

What number am I? _____

> **How many different numbers are 36 when squared?**

The numbers that are 36 when squared are _____

_____

_____

_____

_____

LESSON 5

Find the Pattern

> **A new operation was invented. The symbol for it is #.**

$$7 \# 2 = 16$$
$$7 \# 5 = 19$$
$$3 \# 9 = 15$$
$$4 \# 9 = 17$$
$$5 \# 9 = 19$$
$$15 \# 5 = 35$$

What is 18 # 8? _____

> **What is the pattern for the operation #?**

The pattern for operation # is

_____

_____

_____

_____

> **In this Topic, you learned how to square numbers and reason about quadratic functions.**

Which operation do I perform first when determining the output of a quadratic function?

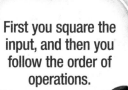

First you square the input, and then you follow the order of operations.

LESSON 1

Express Area and Perimeter as Functions

> **WORKED EXAMPLE**

Write equations to represent the area and perimeter of the figures in the sequence.

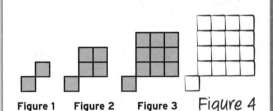

Figure 1   Figure 2   Figure 3   Figure 4

STEP 1 **Extend the sequence.**

STEP 2 **Find the areas.**

Figure Number (n)	Area (ft²)	Perimeter (ft)
1	2	8
2	5	12
3	10	16
4	17	20

$(2 \times 2) + 1 = 5$ ft²
$(3 \times 3) + 1 = 10$ ft²
$(4 \times 4) + 1 = 17$ ft²

STEP 3 **Find the perimeters.**
$(4 \times 2) + 4 = 12$ ft
$(4 \times 3) + 4 = 16$ ft
$(4 \times 4) + 4 = 20$ ft

STEP 4 **Write equations to represent the situations.**

Area: $A = n^2 + 1$
Perimeter: $P = 4n + 4$

> **TRY IT**

1 Write an equation to represent the perimeter of the figures in the sequence.

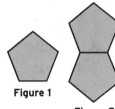

Figure 1

Figure 2

Perimeter: _____

> **GUIDED LEARNING**

2 Write equations to represent the area and perimeter of the figures in the sequence.

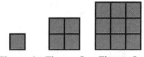

Figure 1   Figure 2   Figure 3

STEP 1 **Extend the sequence.**

STEP 2 **Find the areas.**

Figure Number (n)	Area (cm²)	Perimeter (cm)
1	1	4
2		
3		
4		

STEP 3 **Find the perimeters.**

STEP 4 **Write equations to represent the situations.**

Area:
Perimeter:

> PRACTICE

3 Write equations to represent the area and perimeter of the figures in the sequence.

Figure 1
Figure 2
Figure 3

STEP 1 **Extend the sequence.**

STEP 2 **Find the areas.**

Figure Number (n)	Area (m²)	Perimeter (m)
1	4	10
2		
3		
4		

STEP 3 **Find the perimeters.**

STEP 4 **Write equations to represent the situations.**

Area:
Perimeter:

4 Write equations to represent the area and perimeter of the figures in the sequence.

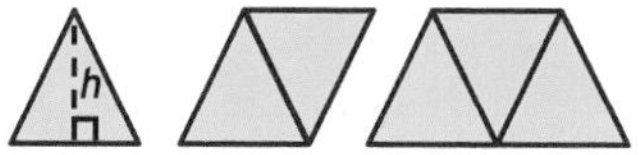

Figure 1 Figure 2   Figure 3

STEP 1 **Extend the sequence.**

STEP 2 **Find the areas.**

Figure Number (n)	Area (yd²)	Perimeter (yd)
1	$\frac{1}{2}h$	3
2		
3		
4		

STEP 3 **Find the perimeters.**

STEP 4 **Write equations to represent the situations.**

Area:
Perimeter:

EXIT Ticket

> **Find and fix the error in the equation.**

Figure Number (n)	Area (in.²)	Perimeter (in.)
1	1	4
2	4	8
3	9	12
4	16	16

Area: $A = 2n$
Perimeter: $P = 4n$

There is more than one way to visually interpret a growing pattern. Each expression may look different, but they are equivalent.

BLOCK **8**

TOPIC 3

TOPIC 2

TOPIC 1

Relate Squares and Square Roots

> WORKED EXAMPLE

> TRY IT

> GUIDED LEARNING

A game designer uses a 25-square-inch grid to represent a digital game board. Write an equation to relate the length of the side of this square to the square root of 25.

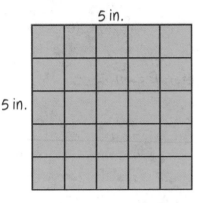

5 in.

5 in.

STEP 1 Express the area of the square as a product.

$$Area = side \times side$$

$$25 \text{ in.}^2 = 5 \text{ in.} \times 5 \text{ in.}$$

STEP 2 Express the product with an exponent.

$$25 = 5^2$$

STEP 3 Express the length of the side as a square root.

$$\sqrt{25} = 5$$

---

1 Jin, an artist, wants to cut a 16 cm² tile into 1-centimeter squares for a mosaic. Draw lines in the square to show how Jin should cut the tile. Then, write an equation to represent the area.

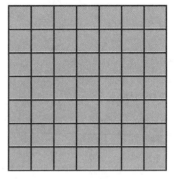

$$Area = length \times width$$

$$Area = side \times side$$

---

2 A digital map designer uses a 49-square-inch grid. Write an equation to relate the length of the side of this square to the square root of 49.

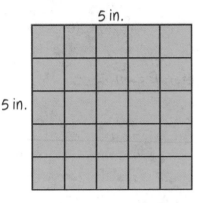

STEP 1 Express the area of the square as a product.

$$Area = side \times side$$

STEP 2 Express the product with an exponent.

STEP 3 Express the length of the side as a square root.

> PRACTICE

3 Write an equation to relate the length of the side of an 81-square-foot grid to the square root of 81.

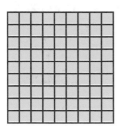

Area = side × side

4 Write an equation to relate the length of the side of a 64-square-yard grid to the square root of 64.

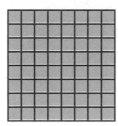

Area = side × side

5 Write an equation to relate the length of the side of a 100-square-inch grid to the square root of 100.

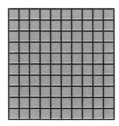

Area = side × side

6 Write an equation to relate the length of the side of a 144-square-inch grid to the square root of 144.

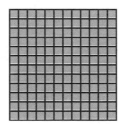

Area = side × side

EXIT Ticket

BLOCK **8**

TOPIC 3

> **Select all that apply.**

Lizzy, a disc jockey, uses a 121 m2 stage. Which of these statements are true?

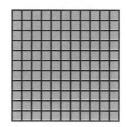

☐ The area of Lizzy's stage is 121 square meters.

☐ The length of one side of Lizzy's stage can be found by dividing 121 ÷ 2.

☐ The equation 121 m^2 = 11 m × 11 m represents the area of Lizzy's stage.

☐ 11^2 = 11 × 2

TOPIC 2

> **Which statement(s) did you select?**

I selected _____

_____ because _____

_____

_____

_____

TOPIC 1

SCORE ⓪ ① ②

0 = Incorrect or No Response
1 = Partial Response
2 = Complete and Accurate

Square a Number to Evaluate a Function

If $x = 4$, what is the output of $y = 2x^2 + 5$?

STEP 1 Substitute the value of x.

$y = 2x^2 + 5$

$y = 2(4)^2 + 5$

STEP 2 Evaluate the square.

$y = 2(4)(4) + 5$

$y = 2(16) + 5$

STEP 3 Find the product.

$y = 32 + 5$

STEP 4 Find the sum.

$y = 37$

Solution: $(4, 37)$

1

If $x = 4$, what is the output of $y = x^2 + 2$?

Solution: $(4, \underline{\hspace{1cm}})$

2

If $x = -3$, what is the output of $y = 3x^2 + 2$?

STEP 1 Substitute the value of x.

$y = 3x^2 + 2$

STEP 2 Evaluate the square.

STEP 3 Find the product.

STEP 4 Find the sum.

Solution:

order of operations *(n)* the sequence in which operations are performed

sum *(n)* the result of addition

> PRACTICE

3 If $x = -4$, what is the output of $y = x^2 + 13$?

$y = x^2 + 13$

Solution:

4 If $x = -1$, what is the output of $y = 4x^2 + 1$?

$y = 4x^2 + 1$

Solution:

5 If $x = 3$, what is the output of $y = x^2 + 2x + 1$?

$y = x^2 + 2x + 1$

Solution:

6 If $x = -2$, what is the output of $y = x^2 - 4x - 12$?

$y = x^2 - 4x - 12$

Solution:

EXIT Ticket

BLOCK **8**

TOPIC 3

> **Solve the problem.**

If $x = -4$, what is the output of $y = 3x^2 + 1$?

$y = 3x^2 + 1$

TOPIC 2

Solution:

> **Compare the ordered pairs for the function $y = 3x^2 + 1$ when $x = 4$ and when $x = -4$. Identify a similarity and a difference.**

A similarity is _____

_____

_____

TOPIC 1

A difference is _____

_____

_____

_____

SCORE (0)(1)(2)   0 = Incorrect or No Response
1 = Partial Response
2 = Complete and Accurate

> **WORKED EXAMPLE**

> **TRY IT**

> **GUIDED LEARNING**

The graph represents a quadratic function. Find the values of x when $y = 3$.

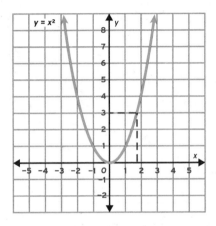

STEP 1 Substitute the value of y.

$$y = x^2$$
$$3 = x^2$$
$$\sqrt{3} = x \text{ or } x = \sqrt{3}$$

STEP 2 Estimate the value of x.

Estimate: _between 1 and 2_

STEP 3 Calculate the value of x.

$$x \approx \underline{1.73}$$

STEP 4 Use symmetry to find the negative solution.

Solutions: $(-1.73, 3)$
$\qquad\quad (1.73, 3)$

1

Use the coordinate plane to plot points that satisfy the equation $y = x^2$ when $x = 2$ and $x = -2$.

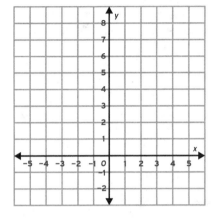

$$y = x^2 \qquad\qquad y = x^2$$

$(-2, \underline{\hspace{1cm}})$ $\qquad$ $(2, \underline{\hspace{1cm}})$

2

The graph represents a quadratic function. Find the values of x when $y = 6$.

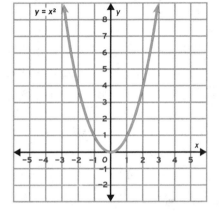

STEP 1 Substitute the value of y.

$$y = x^2$$

STEP 2 Estimate the value of x.

Estimate: _____

STEP 3 Calculate the value of x.

$$x \approx \underline{\hspace{1cm}}$$

STEP 4 Use symmetry to find the negative solution.

Solutions:

BLOCK 8

quadratic function *(n)* a function for which the greatest exponent of x is 2

line of symmetry *(n)* a line that divides a plane figure or graph into two identical parts

› PRACTICE

3

The graph represents a quadratic function. Find the values of x when $y = 5$.

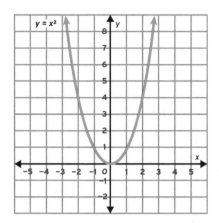

STEP 1 Substitute the value of y.
$$y = x^2$$

STEP 2 Estimate the value of x.

Estimate: _____

STEP 3 Calculate the value of x.

$x \approx$ _____

STEP 4 Use symmetry to find the negative solution.

Solutions:

4

The graph represents a quadratic function. Find the values of x when $y = 8$.

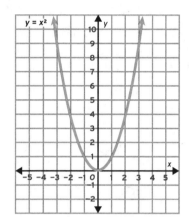

STEP 1 Substitute the value of y.
$$y = x^2$$

STEP 2 Estimate the value of x.

Estimate: _____

STEP 3 Calculate the value of x.

$x \approx$ _____

STEP 4 Use symmetry to find the negative solution.

Solutions:

› **Solve the problem.**

The graph represents a quadratic function. Find the values of x when $y = 2$.

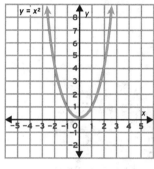

$$y = x^2$$

Estimate: _____

$x \approx$ _____

› **Can the y-value on this graph ever be negative? How do you know?**

The y-value on this graph _____ ever be negative _____

_____

_____

_____

TOPIC 3

TOPIC 2

TOPIC 1

SCORE ⓪ ① ②

0 = Incorrect or No Response
1 = Partial Response
2 = Complete and Accurate

ANCHOR VIDEO CONNECTION

As the Anchor Video shows, you can use functions to describe data using inputs and outputs.

Find the Sum of Two Functions

> You are a video game designer. Today, you are watching two of your employees testing a new game.

Your task is to analyze the data to make predictions about the user experience. You want to know how many points Mai and Tim, the video game testers, will earn altogether.

Mai's and Tim's Data

In each round of the game, Mai goes first and Tim goes second.

- In the first round, Mai earns 1 point, and Tim earns 2 points.
- In the next round, Mai earns 3 points, and Tim earns 4 points.
- The sum of Mai's points is represented by the equation $m = r^2$.
- The sum of Tim's points is represented by the equation $t = r^2 + r$.

A CREATE

Use the models to represent the number of points that Mai and Tim earn altogether after r rounds.

Round (r)	Sum of Mai's Points (r^2)	Sum of Tim's Points ($r^2 + r$)	Sum of Mai's and Tim's Points ($s = r^2 + r^2 + r$)
1	$1^2 = 1$	$1^2 + 1 = 2$	
2	$2^2 = 4$	$2^2 + 2 = 6$	
3			
4			
5			

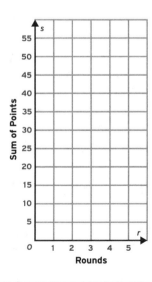

BLOCK 8

BIG IDEA 1 Unlike nonlinear functions, linear functions have a **constant rate of change**.

BIG IDEA 2 Functions can be described with patterns or with **mathematical rules for inputs to find outputs**.

B PREDICT

How many points will Mai and Tim earn altogether after 5 rounds?

_____

_____

_____

_____

_____

_____

C EXPLAIN

Ken found the total number of points after 5 rounds by listing the number of points Mai and Tim earned and adding the 10 numbers. Is this the best method?

_____

_____

_____

_____

_____

_____

EXIT Ticket

BLOCK 8

TOPIC 3

TOPIC 2

TOPIC 1

> **Solve the problem.**

Adam, a game programmer, wrote a game where the blue team goes first in each round and the red team goes second.

• Round 1: blue scores 1 point, then red scores 2.

• Round 2: blue scores 3 points, then red scores 4.

If they continue taking turns and scoring 1 more point than the other every round, how many points will the red team have after 20 rounds?

The red team will have _____ points.

I can use functions to find the sum of the numbers in a pattern.

SCORE ⓪ ① ②

0 = Incorrect or No Response
1 = Partial Response
2 = Complete and Accurate

PERFORMANCE TASK

> **YOUR JOB**
> App Designer

....

> **YOUR TASK**
> Create game boards with increasing sizes.

ANCHOR VIDEO CONNECTION

....

As the Anchor Video shows, many functions in the information technology industry are nonlinear.

Design a Game Board

> **You are designing square grids for a game board. As the levels of the game increase, the size of the game boards increases. Each game board must be square-shaped.**

A EXPLORE

Complete the table to show the number of each type of square game board. Then, write equations as described. In Apply, you will use your equations to design your game board.

Level (x)	Corner Squares (a)	Side Squares (b)	Middle Squares (c)	Total Squares
0				
1				
2				
3				
4				

a	b	a
b	c	b
a	b	a

Key:

$a =$

$b =$

$c =$

Let a represent the number of corner squares, let b represent the number of side squares, and let c represent the number of middle squares. Write equations to find corner squares, side squares, and middle squares for any x-level game.

Corner Squares: _____

Side Squares: _____

Middle Squares: _____

B APPLY

Use your equations to complete the table with the missing numbers of squares.

Level (x)	Corner Squares (a)	Side Squares (b)	Middle Squares (c)	Total Squares
5	4			
6	4	24		
7	4		49	
8	4			100

C ANALYZE

EXPLAIN Which of the equations represent functions that are linear? Nonlinear? How do you know?

____

____

____

____

____

____

REFLECT For levels 0 and 4, the number of side squares is equal to the number of middle squares. Is there any other level for which this is true? ______________________________

____

____

____

____

____

Evaluate

> **Rate how well you and your partner understood and completed each part of the performance task.**

Ranking Scale			
None	Limited	Partial	Thorough
0	1	2	3

A Accurately completed the table.

Me	0	1	2	3
Partner	0	1	2	3

B Correctly modeled the situation with equations.

Me	0	1	2	3
Partner	0	1	2	3

C Answered each question thoughtfully.

Me	0	1	2	3
Partner	0	1	2	3

EXTEND

Write an equation to represent the number of squares for any level game board altogether.

____

____

____

____

BLOCK 8 MINDSET STRATEGY

Reflect on Learning From Mistakes
Congratulations! You've completed Block 8 of *MATH 180*.

Learning From Video Games

Can you imagine playing video games for a living? It might sound easy, but according to Jonathan Wendel, being a professional gamer takes discipline. Even at the top level, the way to win games is by focusing on the losses.

Learning From Mistakes

Wendel believes that **learning from mistakes** is how he consistently comes out on top. He has learned that everyone makes mistakes, but not everyone pays attention to how to learn from them. This strategy has worked. In 2010 he was one of the first people inducted into the International Video Gaming Hall of Fame.

Road to Improvement

It's not just in video games. Everyone makes mistakes—especially in math. The more you learn from those mistakes, the faster you can improve!

Jonathan Wendel, professional video gamer (right)

Don't just blow off your weaknesses. Spend sometimes a full day on just that one thing. You'll definitely appreciate it when it comes to tournament time.

—Jonathan Wendel, on Fnatic.com

> **What is one mistake you made in the past week either in school or at home?**

_____

_____

_____

_____

> **What can you do to learn from that mistake?**

_____

_____

_____

_____

> **Name one time you were afraid to do something because you might make a mistake.**

_____

_____

_____

_____

How to Handle a Mistake

> Here's how to learn from a mistake.

Accept It
Mistakes are a normal part of learning and of life. Everyone makes them!

Learn From It
Understand what you did wrong, and practice doing it right.

Ask for Feedback
Others may have information to help you improve.

Change Your Game
Your first strategy didn't work, so try a new one.

TIPS

Make Connections
- Learning one thing makes learning the next thing easier as you build a strong network in your brain.

Learn With Others
- Explaining something to someone else is the best way to be sure you understand.
- Study with a friend because you can share your strengths!

Learning From Mistakes in *MATH 180*

> **How much do you agree or disagree with this statement?**

I try new math that challenges me even if I might make a mistake.

Select which one applies the most:

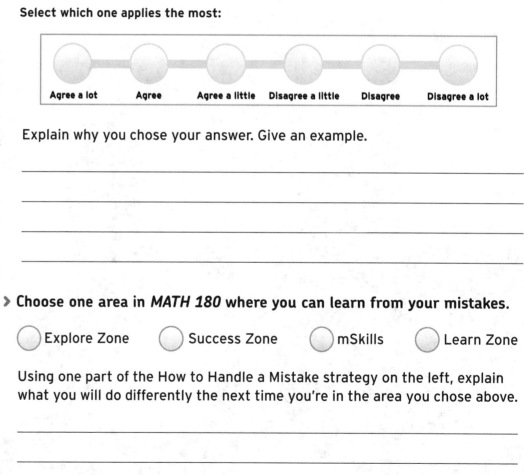

Agree a lot   Agree   Agree a little   Disagree a little   Disagree   Disagree a lot

Explain why you chose your answer. Give an example.

_____

_____

_____

_____

> **Choose one area in *MATH 180* where you can learn from your mistakes.**

◯ Explore Zone   ◯ Success Zone   ◯ mSkills   ◯ Learn Zone

Using one part of the How to Handle a Mistake strategy on the left, explain what you will do differently the next time you're in the area you chose above.

_____

_____

_____

_____

VOCABULARY

function

initial value

intersection

output

rate of change

solution

system of equations

x-intercept

Out on a Limb

How do you replace an arm?

In this Anchor Video, you'll see how doctors are turning to 3-D printing to help people who have lost organs or limbs.

Math in Health Science

In this Block, see how systems of equations are used in health science.

Nutritionists

recommend the daily amount of fats, carbohydrates, and proteins to clients. They look at the **percent breakdown** of each ingredient in different foods and use **linear equations**. Then, they recommend a balanced diet.

Medical Researchers

determine how effective two treatments are by **plotting** their effects on the **same graph**.

Zoo Veterinarians

use **linear equations** to balance diets consisting of crickets and earthworms for different reptiles. Both are about **50% protein**, but a cricket contains about **5 times** as much fat as an earthworm.

Dentists

use **linear equations** to compare the health of teeth treated with two different treatments to see which cleans more effectively.

MRI Technicians

use MRI scanners to see inside a patient's body. The magnetic fields produced by the machine are at least **30,000 times** as strong as the magnetic field surrounding Earth.

Block Preview

> Read the Career Explorations on *mSpace* page 179. Which career interests you the most? Why?

The career that interests me the

most is _____

because _____

_____

_____

> How is math used in careers in health science?

Math is used in careers in health

science when _____

_____

_____

_____

_____

Brain Teaser

> Find the values of ●, ▲, and ■.

- A = 6
- B = 12
- The sums of each row and column are in the circles.

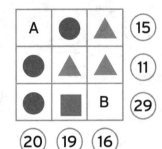

● = _____   ▲= _____   ■ = _____

> Why could you not solve a row first?

I could not solve a row first

because _____

_____

_____

_____

_____

Who's Right?

> Dr. Holmes and Dr. Lee both claim to have seen more patients in 3 days.

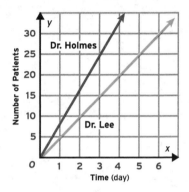

Who's right? _____

> Explain your reasoning.

I know _____ is right because

_____

_____

_____

_____

_____

LESSON 4

Which Does Not Belong?

> Circle the equation that does not belong.

$y = 3x + 6$	$y = -4x + 3$
$y = 2x + 4$	$y = x + 1$

> Explain how you identified the equation that does not belong.

The equation _____

does not belong because _____

_____

_____

_____

_____

LESSON 5

Brain Arcade

> Circle three equivalent tiles to make a match.

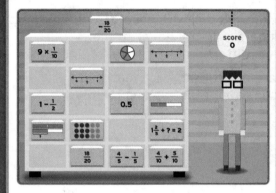

- _____
- _____
- _____

> Create three tiles that are equivalent to $-\frac{18}{20}$ and would make a match.

- _____
- _____
- _____

Sum It Up!

> In this Topic, you learned to compare two linear functions using tables, graphs, and equations.

How can I use a graph to compare two linear functions?

You can use a graph to find the point of intersection. This is the point where both functions have the same output for a given input.

LESSON 1
PROBLEM SOLVING

> EXPLORE

ANCHOR VIDEO CONNECTION

As the Anchor Video shows, health professionals use algebraic reasoning to compare quantities.

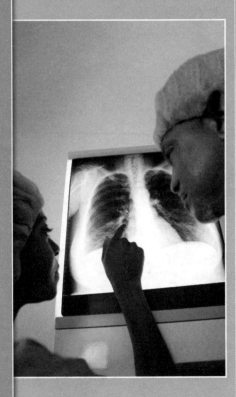

Compare Unknown Quantities

> You are a wellness coach for a fitness center. Today, you are organizing tug-of-war matches with kickboxers, runners, and weightlifters.

- All kickboxers pull with equal strength.
- All runners pull with equal strength.
- All weightlifters pull with equal strength.

Analyze the results of each match to make predictions about the winning teams.

Tug-of-War Matches

	Team A	Team B	Outcome
Match 1	4 kickboxers	5 runners	TIE
Match 2	1 weightlifter	2 runners 1 kickboxer	TIE
Match 3	3 kickboxers 1 weightlifter	5 runners	

A CREATE

Create expressions, equations, ratios, or visual models to represent the relationships of the pulling strengths between the members of different groups.

BLOCK 9

BIG IDEA **1** Flexibility in expressing quantities and the relationships between them allows us to **analyze different quantities**.

BIG IDEA **2** **Algebraic reasoning** is a way to express, understand, and compare relationships between functions.

B PREDICT

Which team will win match 3? Explain your reasoning.

_____

_____

_____

_____

_____

_____

C EXPLAIN

The weightlifters challenge 4 kickboxers and 5 runners. What is the least number of weightlifters needed to win this match?

_____

_____

_____

_____

_____

_____

EXIT Ticket

> **Solve the problem.**

Which team will win match 4?

	Team A	Team B
Match 4	1 weightlifter 3 runners	4 kickboxers

Team _____ will win match 4.

> **Explain your reasoning.**

_____

_____

_____

_____

_____

_____

_____

_____

_____

SCORE ⓪ ① ② | 0 = Incorrect or No Response
1 = Partial Response
2 = Complete and Accurate

BLOCK **9**

TOPIC 3

TOPIC 2

TOPIC 1

Compare Linear Functions Using a Table

> **WORKED EXAMPLE**

A vet gives a sick horse two medications. The horse starts with 600 mg of medication B, and is given 900 mg more every 6 hours. Which medication does the horse have a greater total dose of at 18 hours?

STEP 1 Complete the table.

	Total Dose (mg)	
Time (h)	Medication A	Medication B
0	1200	600
6	1800	1500
12	2400	2400
18	3000	3300
24	3600	4200

STEP 2 Compare the initial values.

The horse starts with a greater total dose of medication ___A___.

STEP 3 Find the input for which both functions have the same output.

The total doses are the same at ___12___ hours.

STEP 4 Compare the outputs of the functions.

The horse has a greater total dose of medication ___B___ at 18 hours.

> **TRY IT**

1 A hospital moves equipment to a new wing. The old wing starts with equipment in 100 rooms. The equipment is moved out of the old wing at 12 rooms per week. Complete the table. Determine which wing will have the greater number of rooms with equipment at 5 weeks.

	Number of Rooms With Equipment	
Time (wk)	New Wing	Old Wing
0	0	100
1	10	88
2	20	
3	30	64
4	40	
5	50	

The _____ wing will have the greater number of rooms with equipment at 5 weeks.

> **GUIDED LEARNING**

2 A nurse uses a portable heart monitor and a portable light. The battery for the light starts with a charge of 88% and loses 8% every 10 minutes. Which device has the greater battery charge at 50 minutes?

STEP 1 Complete the table.

	Battery Charge (%)	
Time (min)	Heart Monitor	Light
0	100	
10	88	
20	76	
30	64	
40	52	
50	40	

STEP 2 Compare the initial values.

The _____ starts with the greater charge.

STEP 3 Find the input for which both functions have the same output.

The devices have the same charge at _____ minutes.

STEP 4 Compare the outputs of the functions.

The _____ has the greater charge at 50 minutes.

initial value *(n)* the starting or first value of a function; often the value of *y* when *x* = 0

PRACTICE

3 Mary and Luis receive dialysis treatments to remove harmful waste from their bloodstreams. Luis starts with 50 mg of waste per deciliter of blood. 7 mg of waste is removed from Luis's bloodstream per hour. Will Mary or Luis have less waste in their bloodstream at 3 hours?

	Amount of Waste (mg)	
Time (h)	Mary	Luis
0	48	
1	42	
2	36	
3	30	
4	24	
5	18	

_____ starts with a greater amount of bloodstream waste.

The amount of bloodstream waste is the same at _____ hours.

_____ has less bloodstream waste at 3 hours.

4 A hospital director is deciding whether to buy or lease a new X-ray machine. To buy the machine, the director would make an initial payment of $4000 and pay $1000 per year. Will the total cost be less after 5 years if the director buys or leases the X-ray machine?

	Total Cost ($)	
Time (yr)	Leasing	Buying
0	0	
1	2000	
2	4000	
3	6000	
4	8000	
5	10,000	

_____ the X-ray machine starts with the lesser cost.

The total costs are the same at _____ years.

The total cost will be less after 5 years if the director _____ the X-ray machine.

EXIT Ticket

BLOCK **9**

TOPIC 3

> Solve the problem.

A trainer compares the calories Jordan and Nico burn as they run. Jordan burned 60 calories before his run. Nico starts with 0 calories burned. Nico burns 75 calories per mile. Who has burned more calories after 5 miles?

	Total Calories Burned	
Distance (mi)	Jordan	Nico
0	60	
1	120	
2	180	
3	240	
4	300	
5	360	

After 5 miles, _____ has burned more calories.

> Will your answer change if you find who burned more calories after 7 miles?

My answer will / will not change because _____

_____

_____

_____

_____

SCORE ⓪ ① ②

| 0 = Incorrect or No Response |
| 1 = Partial Response |
| 2 = Complete and Accurate |

TOPIC 2

TOPIC 1

Comparing Linear Functions **185**

Compare Functions Using a Graph

> WORKED EXAMPLE

> TRY IT

> GUIDED LEARNING

Two hospitals offer jobs to Dr. Brandt. The offer from Glory Hospital is shown on the graph. Hope Hospital offers a $16,000 signing bonus and a salary of $8000 per month. At which hospital would Dr. Brandt earn more in the first 3 months?

STEP 1 Graph the other function.

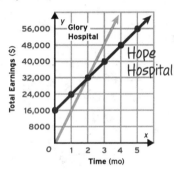

STEP 2 Compare the initial values.

Initially, Dr. Brandt would earn more at _Hope Hospital_.

STEP 3 Find the input for which both functions have the same output.

The total earnings are equal at __2__ months.

STEP 4 Compare the outputs for the given input.

Dr. Brandt will earn more in the first 3 months at _Glory Hospital_.

---

1 A stress test technician is deciding whether to buy or lease a new treadmill. To buy the treadmill, she would make an initial payment of $500 and pay $75 per month. Will the total cost be less after 5 months if the technician buys or leases the treadmill?

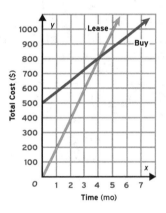

The total cost will be less after 5 months if the technician _____ the treadmill.

---

2 A scientist studies the spread of viruses using a computer program. The spread of virus A is shown on the graph. Virus B starts with 20 affected people and affects 10 more people per day. According to the program, which virus will affect more people in 5 days?

STEP 1 Graph the other function.

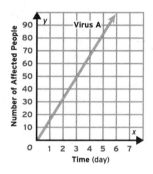

STEP 2 Compare the initial values.

Initially, virus _____ affects more people.

STEP 3 Find the input for which both functions have the same output.

The viruses will affect the same number of people in _____ days.

STEP 4 Compare the outputs for the given input.

Virus _____ will affect more people in 5 days.

> PRACTICE

3

Mobile clinics give flu shots during the winter. The total number of flu shots given at Care Clinic is shown on the graph. Comfort Clinic gave 20 flu shots at its opening and then 10 flu shots per hour. Which clinic gave more flu shots in 6 hours?

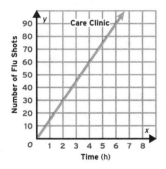

Initially, _____ gave more flu shots.

Both clinics give the same number of flu shots in _____ hours.

_____ gave more flu shots in 6 hours.

4

Two personal trainers have plans to increase profit at their gym. Erin's plan is shown on the graph. Ken's plan has an initial cost of $100 for new equipment, and then earns $50 per session. Whose plan has a greater profit after the first 8 sessions?

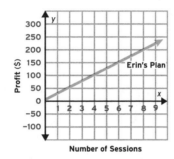

Initially, _____ plan costs less.

Both plans have equal profits after _____ sessions.

_____ plan has a greater profit after the first 8 sessions.

EXIT Ticket

> Solve the problem.

An insurance company has two prescription plans. The total cost for plan C is shown on the graph. Plan D has an initial cost of $20, and then costs $5 per prescription. Which plan costs less when buying 3 prescriptions?

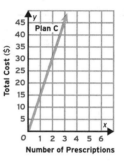

The plans cost the same when buying _____ prescriptions.

Plan _____ costs less when buying 3 prescriptions.

> How did you use the graph to choose the plan that costs less?

I used the graph by _____

_____

_____

_____

_____

SCORE ⓪ ① ②

0 = Incorrect or No Response
1 = Partial Response
2 = Complete and Accurate

BLOCK
9

TOPIC 3

TOPIC 2

TOPIC 1

Compare Functions Using an Equation

> WORKED EXAMPLE

> TRY IT

> GUIDED LEARNING

Function A is represented by the equation $y = 2x + 1$. Function B has an initial value of 8, and its rate of change is −1.5. Which function has a greater output for an input of 4?

STEP 1 Write an equation for the other function.

Function A: $y = 2x + 1$

Function B: $y = -1.5x + 8$

STEP 2 Compare the initial values.

The initial value of function A is ____less____ than function B.

STEP 3 Compare the rates of change.

The rate of change of function A is ____greater____ than function B.

STEP 4 Compare the outputs for the given input.

Function A:
$y = 2x + 1$
$y = 2(4) + 1$
$y = 8 + 1$
$y = 9$

Function B:
$y = -1.5x + 8$
$y = -1.5(4) + 8$
$y = (-6) + 8$
$y = 2$

$9 > 2$

Function ___A___ has a greater output for an input of 4.

1

Function A has an initial value of 10, and its rate of change is 2. Function B is represented by the equation $y = 5x$. Which function has a lesser output for an input of 6?

Function A: $y = 2x + 10$

Function B: $y = 5x$

Function _____ has a lesser output for an input of 6.

2

Function A has an initial value of 35, and its rate of change is 10. Function B is represented by the equation $y = 16x$. Which function has a lesser output for an input of 8?

STEP 1 Write an equation for the other function.

Function A:

Function B: $y = 16x$

STEP 2 Compare the initial values.

The initial value of function A is _____ than function B.

STEP 3 Compare the rates of change.

The rate of change of function A is _____ than function B.

STEP 4 Compare the outputs for the given input.

Function A:

Function B:

Function _____ has a lesser output for an input of 8.

input *(n)* a value substituted for a variable in a function to determine a corresponding output

rate of change *(n)* how fast one quantity changes with respect to another quantity

PRACTICE

3

Function A has an initial value of 50, and its rate of change is −2.5. Function B is represented by the equation $y = 3x$. Which function has a lesser output for an input of 10?

Function A:

Function B:

The initial value of function A is _____ than function B.

The rate of change of function A is _____ than function B.

Function A:

Function B:

Function _____has a lesser output for an input of 10.

4

Function C is represented by the equation $y = 3x + 1$. Function D has an initial value of −1, and its rate of change is 4. Which function has a greater output for an input of 15?

Function C:

Function D:

The initial value of function C is _____ than function D.

The rate of change of function C is _____ than function D.

Function C:

Function D:

Function _____has a greater output for an input of 15.

> **Solve the problem.**

Function A has an initial value of 2, and its rate of change is 2. Function B is represented by the equation $y = 4x − 5$. Which function has a lesser output for an input of 3?

Function _____ has a lesser output for an input of 3.

> **Explain how function B can have a greater rate of change but a lesser output for an input of 3.**

Function B can have a greater rate but a lesser output for an input of 3 because _____

_____

_____

_____

TOPIC 3

TOPIC 2

TOPIC 1

SCORE ⓪ ① ② 0 = Incorrect or No Response
1 = Partial Response
2 = Complete and Accurate

> I notice that the equations are in the form of $y = mx + b$. The ⊙ represents the m and the △ represents the x.

RULES

Guess My Symbol *(Level 1)*

What You Need
- *mSpace* pages 190–193

What to Know
- Both player A and player B record all values for ⊙ at the start of the game.
- Players choose their own order of ⊙-values.
- Values for △ may be used only once.

How to Win
- Calculate total outputs at the end of six turns.
- The player with the greatest total output after six turns is the winner.

> HOW TO PLAY

STEP 1 Players choose and record all values for ⊙.

PLAYER A

TURN	EQUATION
1	___ = ③ · △ + 1
2	___ = ⑤ · △ − 3
3	___ = ⊙(−6) · △ + 2
4	___ = ($\frac{1}{2}$) · △ − 7
5	___ = ⑩ · △ + 14
6	___ = ⊙(−2) · △ − 21

STEP 2 Player A chooses a value for △.

VALUES FOR △

| −14 | −4 | −1 | −$\frac{1}{2}$ | 3 | ⸓ | 11 |

PLAYER A

EQUATION
___ = ③ · △7 + 1

PLAYER B

EQUATION
___ = ⊙(−6) · △7 + 1

STEP 3 Players evaluate and record the output.

PLAYER A

EQUATION	OUTPUT
22 = ③ · △7 + 1 22 = 21 + 1	22

PLAYER B

EQUATION	OUTPUT
−41 = ⊙(−6) · △7 + 1 −41 = −42 + 1	−41

STEP 4 Repeat steps 2–3. Player B chooses △.

PLAYER B

EQUATION	OUTPUT
−41 = ⊙(−6) · △7 + 1 −41 = −42 + 1	−41
25 = ⊙(−2) · △(−14) − 3 25 = 28 − 3	25

PLAYER A

EQUATION	OUTPUT
22 = ③ · △7 + 1 22 = 21 + 1	22
−73 = ⑤ · △(−14) − 3 −73 = −70 − 3	−73

BLOCK 9

RECORDING SHEET

Guess My Symbol

(Level 1)

Record the value of your variables and evaluate the equation to find the output.

VALUES FOR ○					
−6	−2	$\frac{1}{2}$	3	5	10

VALUES FOR △						
−14	−4	−1	$-\frac{1}{2}$	3	7	11

	PLAYER A		PLAYER B	
TURN	EQUATION	OUTPUT	EQUATION	OUTPUT
1	___ = ○ • △ + 1		___ = ○ • △ + 1	
2	___ = ○ • △ − 3		___ = ○ • △ − 3	
3	___ = ○ • △ + 2		___ = ○ • △ + 2	
4	___ = ○ • △ − 7		___ = ○ • △ − 7	
5	___ = ○ • △ + 14		___ = ○ • △ + 14	
6	___ = ○ • △ − 21		___ = ○ • △ − 21	
	TOTAL POINTS		TOTAL POINTS	

RECORDING SHEET
Guess My Symbol
(Level 1)

> Record the value of your variables and evaluate the equation to find the output.

VALUES FOR ○

−6	−2	$\frac{1}{2}$	3	5	10

VALUES FOR △

−14	−4	−1	$-\frac{1}{2}$	3	7	11

	PLAYER A		**PLAYER B**	
TURN	**EQUATION**	**OUTPUT**	**EQUATION**	**OUTPUT**
1	___ = ○ · △ + 1		___ = ○ · △ + 1	
2	___ = ○ · △ − 3		___ = ○ · △ − 3	
3	___ = ○ · △ + 2		___ = ○ · △ + 2	
4	___ = ○ · △ − 7		___ = ○ · △ − 7	
5	___ = ○ · △ + 14		___ = ○ · △ + 14	
6	___ = ○ · △ − 21		___ = ○ · △ − 21	
	TOTAL POINTS		**TOTAL POINTS**	

NUTRITIONISTS help people who want to achieve a specific health-related goal. They advise clients on what to eat and how much to eat in order to lead a healthier lifestyle.

The table shows possible breakfast options for an athlete.

FOOD	CALORIES	QUANTITY	EQUATION	TOTAL CALORIES
Bagel (medium)	288	0.5	$y = 288 \cdot 0.5$	144
Banana (medium)	106	$1\frac{1}{2}$		
Blueberries	1	25	$y = 1 \cdot 25$	25
Corn Flakes	113	1 cup		
Cream Cheese (3 oz)	450	1.5 oz		
Eggs (hard boiled)	72	3		
Grapefruit	32	1		
Skim Milk	90	2 cups		
Whole Milk (1 cup)	146	$\frac{1}{2}$ cup		
Oatmeal	166	$1\frac{1}{2}$ cups		
Peanut Butter (1 tbs)	94	2 tbs		
Sausage (1 link)	81	3 links		
Wheat Toast	75	2		
Waffle (wheat)	74	3		

> Use the table above to calculate a meal of about 750 calories. What would you recommend that an athlete eat for breakfast? _____

_____

_____

> **Solve the problem.**

What is the greatest possible output for the equation below?

VALUES FOR △

−14	−4	−1	$-\frac{1}{2}$	3	7	11

_____ = (−2) • △ − 7

> **How did you solve the problem? Explain.**

I solved the problem by _____

_____

_____

_____

_____

_____

SCORE ⓪ ① ②

| 0 = Incorrect or No Response |
| 1 = Partial Response |
| 2 = Complete and Accurate |

LESSON 1

Brain Teaser

> Solve this number riddle.

- I am a two-digit number.
- The sum of my digits is 8.
- My tens digit is 3 times greater than my ones digit.

I am the number _____.

> How did you begin solving the problem?

I began solving the problem by ____

_____

_____

_____

_____

_____

LESSON 2

Build It

> Choose numbers to make multiple ordered pairs that satisfy the equation $y = 2x + 1$.

| −3 | −2 | −1 | 0 | 1 | 2 | 3 |

> Does the ordered pair (5, 10) satisfy the equation $y = 2x + 1$? Explain.

The ordered pair (5, 10) does / does not satisfy the equation because _____

_____

_____

_____

_____

LESSON 3

Find the Pattern

> Find the pattern in the table to complete the linear equation.

Input x	Output y
0	3
1	5
2	7
3	9
4	11

Equation: $y = $ _____ $x + $ _____

> How did you begin completing the equation?

I began completing the equation by _____

_____

_____

_____

_____

_____

BLOCK 9

LESSON 4

Who's Right?

> Jin and Jonas found different ordered pairs where the two functions have the same *x*- and *y*-values.

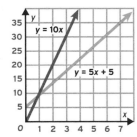

Jin
(1, 10)

Jonas
(2, 20)

Who's right? _____

> Who is correct? How do you know?

I know _____ is correct because

_____

_____

_____

_____

_____

_____

LESSON 5

Brain Arcade

> Circle the bugs with products less than 60.

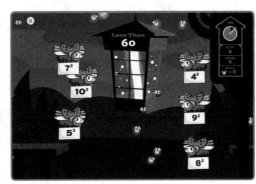

- _____
- _____
- _____

> Which bug has a product greater than 60, but less than 80? Explain.

The bug with _____ has a product greater than 60 and less than 80 because _____

_____

_____

_____

_____

_____

_____

> In this Topic, you learned to analyze a system of two linear equations and reason about its solution.

What does the point of intersection of two linear functions represent on a graph?

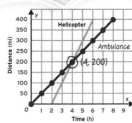

The point of intersection is the solution to the system of equations. It represents the point where both functions have the same *x*- and *y*-values.

LESSON 1
PROBLEM SOLVING

Solve Problems With Equations

> **WORKED EXAMPLE**

Solve for x in the equation.

STEP 1 Simplify the equation.

$$3x + 6 = 4x + 5$$
$$3x - 3x + 6 = 4x - 3x + 5$$
$$0 + 6 = x + 5$$
$$6 = x + 5$$

STEP 2 Solve the equation.

$$6 - 5 = x + 5 - 5$$
$$1 = x \text{ or } x = 1$$

STEP 3 Check your work.

$$3x + 6 = 4x + 5$$
$$3(1) + 6 = 4(1) + 5$$
$$3 + 6 = 4 + 5$$
$$9 = 9$$

> **TRY IT**

1 Solve for x in the equation.

$$3x + 2x = 3 + 2$$

> **GUIDED LEARNING**

2 Solve for y in the equation.

STEP 1 Simplify the equation.

$$5y - 12 = 3y - 8$$

STEP 2 Solve the equation.

STEP 3 Check your work.

$$5y - 12 = 3y - 8$$

BLOCK 9

term *(n)* a number, a variable, or the product of numbers and variables separated by a plus sign or a minus sign

▶ PRACTICE

3 Solve for *n* in the equation.

$$3n + 2 = 6n - 7$$

Check: $3n + 2 = 6n - 7$

4 Solve for *m* in the equation.

$$-9m + 2 = m - 8$$

Check: $-9m + 2 = m - 8$

▶ Select all that apply.

Which of the following equations are true for all values of *x*?

- ☐ $2x + 3x = 5x$

- ☐ $2x + 3x = 6x$

- ☐ $x + 3x = 4x$

- ☐ $2x + 10 - 10 = 2x + 10$

- ☐ $1 = 1 - 5x + 5x$

TOPIC 3

TOPIC 2

TOPIC 1

I can eliminate terms from sides of an equation with inverse operations.

SCORE ⓪ ① ②   0 = Incorrect or No Response
1 = Partial Response
2 = Complete and Accurate

LESSON 2

CONCEPT

Compare x-Intercepts

> WORKED EXAMPLE

Bart and Robin take a health survey. The equations $y = -1x + 6$ and $y = -0.5x + 6$ model the time it takes them to complete it. Compare the times when Bart and Robin complete the survey.

STEP 1 Find the x-intercepts.

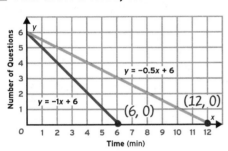

STEP 2 Verify the first x-intercept.

Bart: $y = -1x + 6$

$0 = -1(6) + 6$
$0 = -6 + 6$
$0 = 0$

STEP 3 Verify the other x-intercept.

Robin: $y = -0.5x + 6$

$0 = -0.5(12) + 6$
$0 = -6 + 6$
$0 = 0$

STEP 4 Analyze the intercepts.

$12 - 6 = 6$

Bart completes the survey
__6 minutes before__ Robin.

> TRY IT

1

A patient receives two medications, which are released at different rates from IV bags. The graph shows the volume of medication released over time. Compare the times when the medications run out.

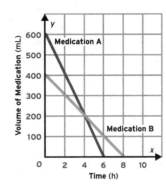

Medication A: $y = -100x + 600$

Medication B: $y = -50x + 400$

Medication A runs out in _____ hours.

Medication B runs out in _____ hours.

Medication A runs out _____ hours
before / after medication B.

> GUIDED LEARNING

2

Scientists freeze two medical samples. The equations $y = -2x + 70$ and $y = -1x + 60$ model the temperatures of the samples. Compare the times when the samples reach a temperature of 0°C.

STEP 1 Find the x-intercepts.

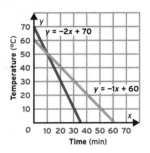

STEP 2 Verify the first x-intercept.

Sample A: $y = -2x + 70$

STEP 3 Verify the other x-intercept.

Sample B: $y = -1x + 60$

STEP 4 Analyze the intercepts.

Sample A reaches 0°C

_____ sample B.

> PRACTICE

3

A nurse tests the time it takes two heart monitor batteries to reach no charge. The equations $y = -3x + 9$ and $y = -1.5x + 6$ model the charge of the batteries. Compare the times when the batteries reach no charge.

STEP 1 Find the *x*-intercepts.

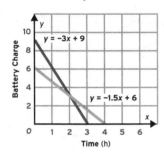

STEP 2 Verify the first *x*-intercept.

Battery A: $y = -3x + 9$

STEP 3 Verify the other *x*-intercept.

Battery B: $y = -1.5x + 6$

STEP 4 Analyze the intercepts.

Battery A reaches no charge

_____ battery B.

4

A rescue team tests the time it takes two freezers to reach a temperature of 0°C. The equations $y = -0.5x + 5$ and $y = -2x + 10$ model the freezer temperatures. Compare the times when the freezers reach 0°C.

STEP 1 Find the *x*-intercepts.

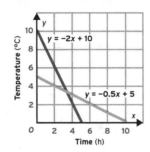

STEP 2 Verify the first *x*-intercept.

First freezer: $y = -0.5x + 5$

STEP 3 Verify the other *x*-intercept.

Second freezer: $y = -2x + 10$

STEP 4 Analyze the intercepts.

The first freezer reaches 0°C

_____ the second freezer.

EXIT
Ticket

BLOCK
9

> **Solve the problem.**

Todd and Gemma take a health test. The graph shows the time it takes them to complete the test. Label the *x*-intercepts.

Todd: $y = -\frac{4}{3}x + 4$

Gemma: $y = -\frac{1}{2}x + 4$

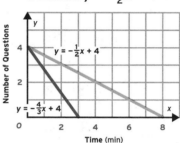

> **A researcher concludes that Todd completed 4 minutes before Gemma. Is the researcher correct?**

The researcher is / is not correct because _____

_____

_____

_____

_____

_____

_____

_____

TOPIC 3

TOPIC 2

TOPIC 1

SCORE ⓪ ① ② | 0 = Incorrect or No Response
1 = Partial Response
2 = Complete and Accurate

LESSON 3
CONCEPT

Reason About a System of Linear Equations

> **WORKED EXAMPLE**

Joe and Abe receive medication from an IV line. Joe's IV drips at 50 mL per hour. Abe's IV drips at 45 mL per hour. Abe starts with 15 mL of medication. When will Joe and Abe receive the same amount of medication?

STEP 1 Find solutions to the first equation.

Joe: $m = 50t$

Abe: $m = 45t + 15$

Time (h)	Volume of Medication (mL)	
	Joe	Abe
0	0	15
1	50	60
2	100	105
→ 3	150	150
4	200	195

STEP 2 Find solutions to the other equation.

STEP 3 Reason about the solutions.

A solution to $m = 50t$: (1, 50)

A solution to $m = 45t + 15$: (1, 60)

The solution to the system: (3, 150)

STEP 4 Interpret the solution to the system.

Joe and Abe will receive 150 mL of medication after 3 hours.

> **TRY IT**

1

At a long-distance race, Deana runs at a speed of 6 mi/h. Lamont runs at a speed of 5 mi/h, but he begins the race 3 miles ahead of Deana. When will Deana reach Lamont?

Deana: $d = 6t$

Lamont: $d = 5t + 3$

Time (h)	Distance (mi)	
	Deana	Lamont
0	0	3
1	6	8
2		
3		
4		

Deana will reach Lamont after

_____ hours and _____ miles.

> **GUIDED LEARNING**

2

A medical officer directs a helicopter and an ambulance to a hospital. The helicopter flies at 120 mi/h. The ambulance drives at 70 mi/h, but starts 100 miles closer to the hospital. When will the helicopter pass the ambulance?

STEP 1 Find solutions to the first equation.

Helicopter: $d = 120t$

Ambulance: $d = 70t + 100$

Time (h)	Distance (mi)	
	Helicopter	Ambulance
0		
1		
2		
3		
4		

STEP 2 Find solutions to the other equation.

STEP 3 Reason about the solutions.

A solution to $d = 120t$: _____

A solution to $d = 70t + 100$: _____

The solution to the system: _____

STEP 4 Interpret the solution to the system.

The helicopter passes the ambulance after _____ hours and _____ miles.

> PRACTICE

3

A hospital patient uses a call button for a doctor. Dr. Gleason walks at a speed of 2 m/s. Dr. Kaiser walks at a speed of 1 m/s, but she is 5 meters closer to the patient's room. When will Dr. Gleason reach Dr. Kaiser?

Dr. Gleason: $d = 2t$

Dr. Kaiser: $d = 1t + 5$

Time (s)	Distance (m)	
	Dr. Gleason	Dr. Kaiser
0		
1		
2		
3		
4		
5		

A solution to $d = 2t$: _____

A solution to $d = 1t + 5$: _____

The solution to the system: _____

Dr. Gleason reaches Dr. Kaiser after _____ seconds and _____ meters.

4

A physical therapist measures the range of motion of two patients' knees after surgery. Barney adds 25 degrees to his range per week. Keli starts with a 10-degree range of motion. She adds 20 degrees to her range per week. When will Barney and Keli have the same range of motion?

Barney: $d = 25t$

Keli: $d = 20t + 10$

Time (wk)	Range of Motion (degrees)	
	Barney	Keli
0		
1		
2		
3		
4		

A solution to $d = 25t$: _____

A solution to $d = 20t + 10$: _____

The solution to the system: _____

Barney and Keli will have the same range of motion after _____ weeks and _____ degrees.

> Solve the problem.

At a health fair race, Shanté runs at a speed of 6 mi/h. Derek starts the race 4 miles past the starting line, and he jogs at a speed of 4 mi/h. When will Shanté pass Derek?

Shanté: $d = 6t$

Derek: $d = 4t + 4$

Time (h)	Distance (mi)	
	Shanté	Derek
0		
1		
2		
3		
4		

Shanté will reach Derek after _____ hours and _____ miles.

TOPIC 3

TOPIC 2

TOPIC 1

A system of equations has a solution at the point where both equations have the same *x*- and *y*-values.

SCORE ⓪ ① ②

0 = Incorrect or No Response
1 = Partial Response
2 = Complete and Accurate

LESSON 4
CONCEPT

Analyze Graphs of Two Linear Functions

> **WORKED EXAMPLE**

A medical team has two options to transport an organ to a hospital 400 miles away. They can wait to take a helicopter, or they can leave in an ambulance immediately. The ambulance drives at 50 mi/h. Which option will get the organ to the hospital in less time?

STEP 1 Analyze the graph of the function.

The helicopter leaves after __2__ hours. It travels at __100__ mi/h.

STEP 2 Plot points to graph the other function.

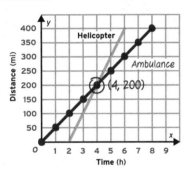

STEP 3 Plot and interpret the point of intersection.

The helicopter will reach the ambulance at __4__ hours and __200__ miles.

STEP 4 Solve the problem.

The __helicopter__ will get the organ to the hospital in less time.

> **TRY IT**

1 Pierre, a veterinarian, has two options for transportation to a zoo 125 miles away. He can wait to take a train, or leave immediately in a taxi. The taxi drives at 25 mi/h. Which option will get Pierre to the zoo in less time?

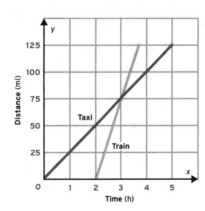

The train will reach the taxi at _____ hours and _____ miles.

The _____ will get Pierre to the zoo in less time.

> **GUIDED LEARNING**

2 Emma has two options for an 80-hour medical program. She can wait and start program A, or she can start program B immediately. Program B requires 10 hours of work per week. Which program allows Emma to complete the hours in less time?

STEP 1 Analyze the graph of the function.

Program A starts after _____ weeks. It requires _____ hours of work per week.

STEP 2 Plot points to graph the other function.

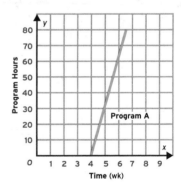

STEP 3 Plot and interpret the point of intersection.

After _____ weeks, Emma will complete _____ class hours in both programs.

STEP 4 Solve the problem.

Program _____ allows Emma to complete the hours in less time.

EXIT Ticket

> PRACTICE

3 An emergency medical team has two options to get to a disaster zone 720 miles away. They can wait to take a helicopter, or they can leave in an ambulance immediately. The ambulance drives at 80 mi/h. Which option will get the team to the disaster zone in less time?

The helicopter leaves after _____ hours. It travels at _____ mi/h.

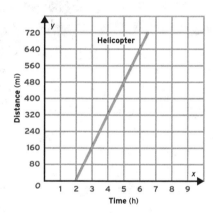

The helicopter will reach the ambulance after _____ hours and _____ miles.

The _____ will get the team to the disaster zone in less time.

4 Ren, a nursing student, has two options for courses that require 36 class hours. She can wait and start Public Health, or she can start Nutrition immediately. Nutrition requires 3 class hours per week. Which course allows Ren to complete the class hours in less time?

Public Health starts after _____ weeks. It has _____ class hours per week.

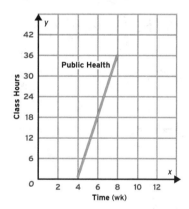

At _____ weeks, Ren will complete _____ class hours in both courses.

_____ allows Ren to complete the class hours in less time.

> **Solve the problem.**

A pharmacy has two prescription plans. Plan Y has an initial cost. Plan Z does not have an initial cost, but the cost of each prescription is $10. Which plan will cost less for a person who gets 6 prescriptions?

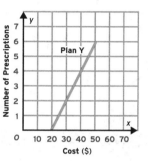

Plan _____ will cost less for a person who gets 6 prescriptions.

> **Fred needs only 2 prescriptions. Which plan costs less for Fred? Explain.**

Plan _____ costs less for Fred because _____

_____

_____

_____

_____

SCORE ⓪ ① ②   0 = Incorrect or No Response
1 = Partial Response
2 = Complete and Accurate

The number given in the first equation helps me choose a value for △. Then I'll think about which quadrant the solution needs to be in to earn the most points.

RULES

Guess My Symbol *(Level 2)*

What You Need

- *mSpace* pages 204–207

What to Know

- The △ and ☐ symbols represent the x and y variables.
- Players represent the equations as functions.

How to Win

- Players earn points by finding the quadrant you find the solutions in.
- The player with the most points after 4 turns is the winner.

> HOW TO PLAY

STEP 1 Choose values for △ and ○.

VALUES FOR △

-4 -3 (-2) -1 1 2 3 5

VALUES FOR ○

-7 -5 -3 -1 2 (4) 6 8

EQUATIONS

☐ = 3 · △-2

☐ = (4) · △-2² + △

STEP 2 Solve for the missing values.

EQUATIONS

 -6 = 3 · △-2

-6 = (4) · △-2² + △-22

$-6 = 4 \cdot (-2)^2 + (-22)$

$-6 = 4 \cdot 4 + (-22)$

$-6 = 16 - 22$

STEP 3 Record the solution and functions.

SOLUTION (△ ☐)	FUNCTIONS
(-2, -6)	$y = 3x$ $y = 4x^2 - 22$

STEP 4 Find the quadrant of the solution and record the number of points earned.

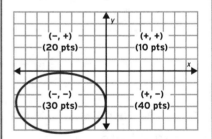

SOLUTION (△, ☐)	FUNCTIONS	POINTS
(-2, -6)	$y = 3x$ $y = 4x^2 - 22$	30

BLOCK 9

RECORDING SHEET
Guess My Symbol
(Level 2)

> Write the equations as functions and record the solution to both functions.

VALUES FOR △

| −4 | −3 | −2 | −1 | 1 | 2 | 3 | 5 |

VALUES FOR ○

| −7 | −5 | −3 | −1 | 2 | 4 | 6 | 8 |

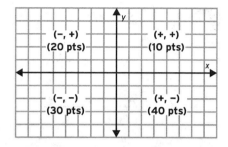

(−, +) (20 pts) (+, +) (10 pts)

(−, −) (30 pts) (+, −) (40 pts)

TURN	EQUATION	SOLUTION (△, □)	FUNCTIONS	POINTS
1	□ = 3 · △ □ = ○ · △² + ▱			
2	□ = −0.5 · △ □ = ○ · △² + ▱			
3	□ = $\frac{3}{2}$ · △ □ = ○ · △² + ▱			
4	□ = −2 · △ □ = ○ · △² + ▱			
			TOTAL POINTS	

BLOCK 9 > TOPIC 2
LESSON 5
GAME

RECORDING SHEET
Guess My Symbol
(Level 2)

> Write the equations as functions and record the solution to both functions.

VALUES FOR △

| −4 | −3 | −2 | −1 | 1 | 2 | 3 | 5 |

VALUES FOR ○

| −7 | −5 | −3 | −1 | 2 | 4 | 6 | 8 |

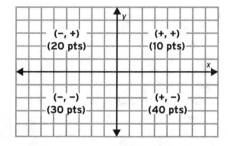

| | | (−, +) (20 pts) | (+, +) (10 pts) |
| | | (−, −) (30 pts) | (+, −) (40 pts) |

TURN	EQUATION	SOLUTION (△, □)	FUNCTIONS	POINTS
1	□ = 2 · △ □ = ○ · △² + ⬠			
2	□ = −$\frac{3}{4}$ · △ □ = ○ · △² + ⬠			
3	□ = 2.5 · △ □ = ○ · △² + ⬠			
4	□ = −$\frac{5}{2}$ · △ □ = ○ · △² + ⬠			
			TOTAL POINTS	

MEDICAL RESEARCHERS conduct medical studies to find the latest breakthroughs in science and medicine. They create experimental trials to see the effects of new medicine and vitamins on test subjects.

The table shows data from a study conducted on the effectiveness of two different vitamins.

Time (h)	QUESTIONS ANSWERED	
	VITAMIN Q $y = 20t$	VITAMIN R $y = 10t + 20$
0	0	20
1		
2		
3		
4		
5		

- Two subjects were awake for 24 hours and given an alertness test.

- A dose of vitamins was given 10 minutes after the start of the test.

- The subject taking vitamin R completes 20 questions before taking the vitamin.

> **Complete the table. When did both subjects answer the same number of questions?** _____

_____

_____

> **Which vitamin was more effective in making a person more alert?**

_____

_____

_____

_____

EXIT Ticket

BLOCK **9**

TOPIC 3

> **Solve the problem.**

Choose a value for △ and ● using the numbers below to create a function with a positive △-value.

| −2 | 3 | 4 | 8 | −10 |

$$\square = 4 \cdot \triangle$$

$$\square = \bigcirc \cdot \triangle^2 + \text{▱}$$

TOPIC 2

TOPIC 1

> **Write the function that represents the second equation. Write its solution as an ordered pair.**

Function: $y = \underline{\hspace{1cm}} x^2 + \underline{\hspace{1cm}}$

Solution: _____

SCORE ⓪ ① ②   0 = Incorrect or No Response
1 = Partial Response
2 = Complete and Accurate

LESSON 1

Brain Teaser

> Solve this number riddle.

- I am a two-digit number.
- The sum of my digits is 12.
- My ones digit is 2 times greater than my tens digit.

I am the number _____.

> How did you begin solving this problem?

To begin solving this problem, _____
_____
_____
_____

LESSON 2

Missing Numbers

> Use the numbers to create two linear equations in $y = mx + b$ form for which the ordered pair (2, 5) is a solution.

| −1 | 0 | 1 | 2 | 3 | 4 |

$$y = \underline{\quad}x + \underline{\quad}$$
$$y = \underline{\quad}x + \underline{\quad}$$

> What does the ordered pair (2, 5) represent for these two equations? The ordered pair (2, 5) represents _____
_____
_____
_____

LESSON 3

Which Does Not Belong?

> Circle the ordered pair that does not belong.

| (2, 0) | (1, 2) | (0, 1) |

| (0, −4) | (3, 0) | (−1, 0) |

> Which ordered pair did you choose? Explain.

I chose _____ because _____
_____
_____
_____

BLOCK 9

LESSON 4

Who's Right?

> When asked about the solution to the system of equations, Ty and Pegah found different answers.

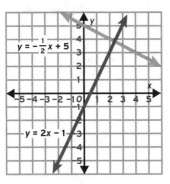

$y = -\frac{1}{2}x + 5$

$y = 2x - 1$

Pegah

(2, 3) is the solution to the system.

Ty

(2, 3) is not the solution to the system.

> Who is right? Explain how you know.

I know _____ is right because

_____

_____

_____

LESSON 5

Find the Pattern

> Which of the numbers is both the greatest in its column and the least in its row?

10	6	4	3	2
11	7	14	10	8
8	3	4	5	9
13	4	15	12	1
8	2	5	9	3

> How did you solve this problem?

First, I _____

_____

Then, I _____

_____

_____

_____

> In this Topic, you learned to solve systems of equations by finding the point of intersection.

Where can I find the solution to a system of equations on a graph?

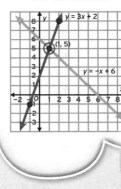

The solution is the point of intersection of the functions.

$y = 3x + 2$

(1, 5)

$y = -x + 6$

LESSON 1
PROBLEM SOLVING

Generate Equations to Solve Problems

The number of patients Juan sees is the sum of 3 times a number and 5. The number of patients Juan sees is also the difference between 4 times the same number and 6. How many patients does Juan see?

STEP 1 Represent the problem.

_P_ represents the _number of patients Juan sees._

_n_ represents the _unknown number._

$$p = 3n + 5$$
$$p = 4n - 6$$

STEP 2 Write an equation with one variable.

$$3n + 5 = 4n - 6$$

STEP 3 Solve for the first variable.

$$3n - 3n + 5 = 4n - 3n - 6$$
$$5 = n - 6$$
$$5 + 6 = n - 6 + 6$$
$$11 = n \text{ or } n = 11$$

STEP 4 Solve for the other variable.

$$p = 3(11) + 5 \qquad p = 4(11) - 6$$
$$p = 33 + 5 \qquad p = 44 - 6$$
$$p = 38 \qquad p = 38$$

Juan sees __38__ patients.

1

The sum of twice a number and 3 is equal to the sum of 3 times the same number and 2. What is the number?

The number is _____.

2

The number of cups of water Carla drinks daily is the difference between 5 times a number and 7. The number of cups of water is also the sum of the same number and 5. How many cups of water does Carla drink daily?

STEP 1 Represent the problem.

_____ represents the _____

_____

_____ represents the _____

_____

STEP 2 Write an equation with one variable.

STEP 3 Solve for the first variable.

STEP 4 Solve for the other variable.

Carla drinks _____ cups of water daily.

system of equations *(n)* two or more equations considered at the same time

linear equation *(n)* an equation whose graph is a straight line

> PRACTICE

3 The number of sit-ups Micah does is the sum of twice a number and 25. The number of sit-ups Micah does is also 3 times the number minus 25. How many sit-ups does Micah do?

_____ represents the _____

_____

_____ represents the _____

_____

Micah does _____ sit-ups.

4 The number of push-ups Nuria does is the sum of 8 times a number and 4. The number of push-ups Nuria does is also the difference between 10 times the number and 20. How many push-ups does Nuria do?

_____ represents the _____

_____

_____ represents the _____

_____

Nuria does _____ push-ups.

TOPIC 3

> *Select all that apply.*

For which equations is the ordered pair (5, 25) a solution?

☐ $y = 5x$

☐ $y = 3x + 12$

☐ $y = x^2$

☐ $y = x + 20$

☐ $y = 4x + 15$

TOPIC 2

> **Write a system of linear equations that has a solution of (5, 25) using two equations from above. Explain your reasoning.**

A system of linear equations that has a solution of (5, 25) is

_____ and _____

because _____

_____

_____

_____

_____

_____

TOPIC 1

SCORE ⓪①②

0 = Incorrect or No Response
1 = Partial Response
2 = Complete and Accurate

Determine If an Ordered Pair Is a Solution

> **WORKED EXAMPLE**

Is the ordered pair (2, 3) the solution to the system of equations: $y = 0.5x + 2$ and $y = -x + 8$?

STEP 1 Determine if the ordered pair is a solution to the first equation.

$$y = 0.5x + 2$$
$$3 = 0.5(2) + 2$$
$$3 = 1 + 2$$
$$3 = 3$$

STEP 2 Determine if the ordered pair is a solution to the other equation.

$$y = -x + 8$$
$$3 = -(2) + 8$$
$$3 = (-2) + 8$$
$$3 \neq 6$$

STEP 3 Determine if the ordered pair is the solution to the system.

The ordered pair (2, 3) __is not__ the solution to the system of equations.

STEP 4 Use the graph to find the solution to the system.

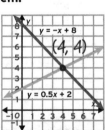

> **TRY IT**

1 Determine if the ordered pair (1, 3) is a solution to $y = -x + 4$, $y = 2x + 1$, or both of the equations.

(1, 3) is / is not a solution to $y = -x + 4$.

(1, 3) is / is not a solution to $y = 2x + 1$.

(1, 3) is / is not a solution to both equations.

> **GUIDED LEARNING**

2 Is the ordered pair (1, 4) the solution to the system of equations: $y = -2x + 6$ and $y = -0.5x + 4.5$?

STEP 1 Determine if the ordered pair is a solution to the first equation.

$$y = -2x + 6$$

STEP 2 Determine if the ordered pair is a solution to the other equation.

$$y = -0.5x + 4.5$$

STEP 3 Determine if the ordered pair is the solution to the system.

The ordered pair (1, 4) _____ the solution to the system of equations.

STEP 4 Use the graph to find the solution to the system.

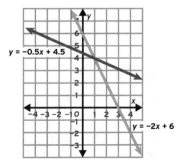

BLOCK 9

> PRACTICE

3

Is the ordered pair (2, −1) the solution to the system of equations:
$y = -4x + 7$ and $y = -x + 4$?

$y = -4x + 7$

$y = -x + 4$

The ordered pair (2, −1) _____ the solution to the system of equations.

Use the graph to find the solution to the system.

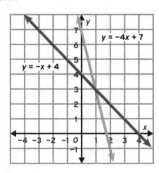

4

Is the ordered pair (2, 1) the solution to the system of equations:
$y = 2x - 3$ and $y = x - 1$?

$y = 2x - 3$

$y = x - 1$

The ordered pair (2, 1) _____ the solution to the system of equations.

Use the graph to find the solution to the system.

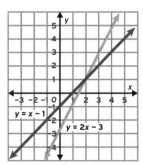

> Solve the problem.

TOPIC 3

Is the ordered pair (−2, 2) the solution to the system of equations: $y = -4x - 6$ and $y = \frac{1}{2}x + 3$?

The ordered pair (−2, 2) _____ the solution to the system of equations.

> **Is it possible for a system of two linear equations to have more than one solution? Why or why not?**

It is / is not possible for a system of two linear equations to have more than one solution because _____

_____

_____

_____

TOPIC 2

TOPIC 1

Solve a System of Linear Equations

> WORKED EXAMPLE

> TRY IT

> GUIDED LEARNING

Graph to find the solution to the system of equations: $y = -2x + 1$ and $y = x + 4$.

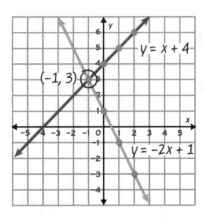

STEP 1 Find the slope and y-intercept of each line.

Line A: $y = -2x + 1$

Slope: _−2_

y-intercept: _1_

Line B: $y = x + 4$

Slope: _1_

y-intercept: _4_

STEP 2 Graph line A.

STEP 3 Graph line B.

STEP 4 Find the solution.

The solution to the system of equations is _(−1, 3)_.

1

Graph to find the solution to the system of equations: $y = x + 1$ and $y = -2x + 4$. Line A is on the graph.

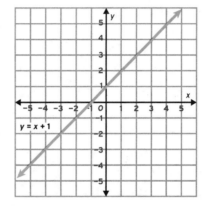

Line A: $y = x + 1$

Line B: $y = -2x + 4$

The solution to the system of equations is _____.

2

Graph to find the solution to the system of equations: $y = -\frac{1}{2}x + 4$ and $y = x - 2$.

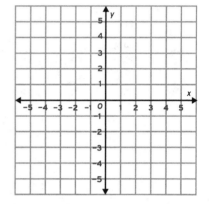

STEP 1 Find the slope and y-intercept of each line.

Line A: $y = -\frac{1}{2}x + 4$

Slope: _____

y-intercept: _____

Line B: $y = x - 2$

Slope: _____

y-intercept: _____

STEP 2 Graph line A.

STEP 3 Graph line B.

STEP 4 Find the solution.

The solution to the system of equations is _____.

system of equations *(n)* two or more equations considered at the same time

y-intercept *(n)* a point where a graph crosses the vertical axis

> PRACTICE

3

Graph to find the solution to the system of equations: $y = -4x + 5$ and $y = -x + 2$.

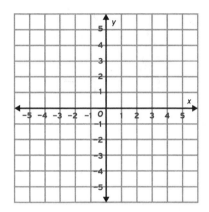

Line A: $y = -4x + 5$

Slope: _____

y-intercept: _____

Line B: $y = -x + 2$

Slope: _____

y-intercept: _____

The solution to the system of equations is _____.

4

Graph to find the solution to the system of equations: $y = x + 1$ and $y = \frac{1}{2}x - 1$.

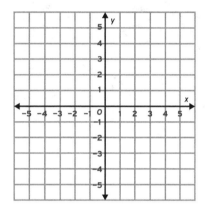

Line A: $y = x + 1$

Slope: _____

y-intercept: _____

Line B: $y = \frac{1}{2}x - 1$

Slope: _____

y-intercept: _____

The solution to the system of equations is _____.

> *Select all that apply.*

Graph line A and line B. Which of these statements is true?

Line A: $y = \frac{1}{2}x + 2$

Line B: $y = 3x - 3$

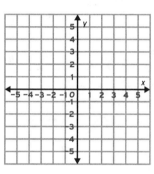

☐ Both lines have positive slopes.

☐ Line A has a negative y-intercept.

☐ Line B has a negative y-intercept.

☐ The solution to the system is (2, −3).

☐ The solution to the system is (2, 3).

☐ The solution lies in quadrant 1.

☐ The solution lies in quadrant 3.

TOPIC 3

TOPIC 2

TOPIC 1

SCORE ⓪ ① ②

0 = Incorrect or No Response
1 = Partial Response
2 = Complete and Accurate

Find Other Solution Sets

> **WORKED EXAMPLE**

> **TRY IT**

> **GUIDED LEARNING**

WORKED EXAMPLE

Function A and function B are shown on the graph. Are (−2, 1), (0, 1), and (3, 1) solutions to the system of equations?

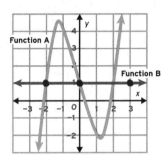

STEP 1 Analyze the functions.

Function A is linear / ⟨nonlinear.⟩

Function B is ⟨linear⟩ / nonlinear.

STEP 2 Determine the number of intersections.

The graph shows ___3___ point(s) of intersection.

STEP 3 Interpret the points.

(−2, 1) ⟨is⟩ / is not a solution to the system because *it is a point of intersection.*

(0, 1) ⟨is⟩ / is not a solution to the system because *it is a point of intersection.*

(3, 1) is / ⟨is not⟩ a solution to the system because *it is not a point of intersection.*

---

1 Function A and function B are shown on the graph. Are (2, 4) and (0, 2) solutions to the system of equations?

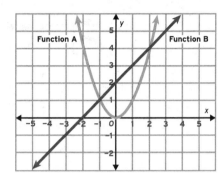

(2, 4) is / is not a solution to the system of equations.

(0, 2) is / is not a solution to the system of equations.

---

2 Function A and function B are shown on the graph. Are (−3, 0) and (3, 0) solutions to the system of equations?

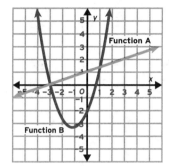

STEP 1 Analyze the functions.

Function A is linear / nonlinear.

Function B is linear / nonlinear.

STEP 2 Determine the number of intersections.

The graph shows _____ point(s) of intersection.

STEP 3 Interpret the points.

(−3, 0) is / is not a solution to the system because _____

_____

(3, 0) is / is not a solution to the system because _____

_____

linear *(adj)* relating to or forming a straight line : nonlinear *(adj)* not forming a line

> **PRACTICE**

3

Function A and function B are shown on the graph. Are (2, 0) and (−2, 5) solutions to the system of equations?

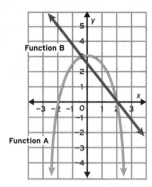

Function A is linear / nonlinear.

Function B is linear / nonlinear.

The graph shows _____ point(s) of intersection.

(2, 0) is / is not a solution to the system because _____
_____

(−2, 5) is / is not a solution to the system because _____
_____

4

Function A and function B are shown on the graph. Are (0, 0), (−2, −2), and (1, 1) solutions to the system of equations?

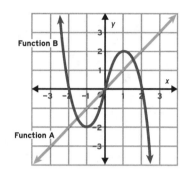

Function A is linear / nonlinear.

Function B is linear / nonlinear.

The graph shows _____ point(s) of intersection.

(0, 0) is / is not a solution to the system because _____
_____

(−2, −2) is / is not a solution to the system because _____
_____

(1, 1) is / is not a solution to the system because _____
_____

> **Find and fix the error.**

Ron found two solutions to the system of equations.

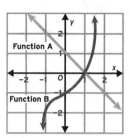

Solution(s): __(0, −1), (1, 0)__

> **What error did Ron make? Explain.**

The error Ron made was _____
_____
_____
_____

A point represents a solution to a system when it's a point of intersection with all the functions in the system.

SCORE ⓪ ① ②

0 = Incorrect or No Response
1 = Partial Response
2 = Complete and Accurate

LESSON 5
PROBLEM SOLVING

> EXPLORE

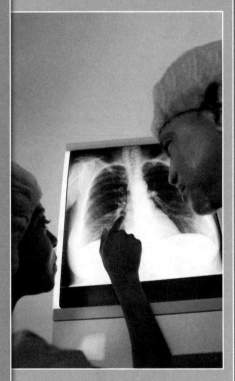

Compare the Growth of Functions

> You are a physical therapist. You are planning a daily exercise program for your client, Kendra. You offer her two plans to choose from.

Exercise Plans

Plan 1: 20 repetitions of exercises each day

Plan 2: Double the number of repetitions until therapy is over. (1 repetition on the first day, 2 repetitions on the second day, 4 repetitions on the third day, etc.)

A CREATE

Complete the table, and graph to compare the number of total repetitions with each plan.

Plan 1		Plan 2		
Time (day)	Total Repetitions	Time (day)	Number of Repetitions That Day	Total Repetitions
1	20	1	1	1
2	40	2	1 • 2 = 2	1 + 2 = 3
3	60	3	2 • 2 = 4	3 + 4 = 7
4		4		
5		5		
6		6		
7		7		
8		8		
9		9		
10		10		

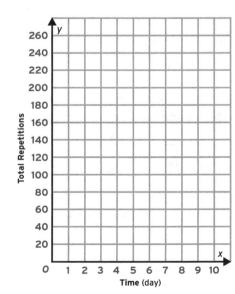

BIG IDEA 1 Flexibility in expressing quantities and the relationships between them allows us to **analyze different quantities**.

BIG IDEA 2 **Algebraic reasoning** helps us express, understand, and compare relationships between functions.

B PREDICT

Kendra will be in physical therapy for 8 days. With which plan will she do more total repetitions? Explain your reasoning.

_____

_____

_____

_____

_____

_____

_____

C EXPLAIN

Choose a plan for Kendra. Explain your reasoning.

_____

_____

_____

_____

_____

_____

_____

_____

EXIT Ticket

BLOCK **9**

TOPIC 3

> **Solve the problem.**

Kendra suggests another exercise plan. It is shown in the table.

Time (day)	Number of Repetitions That Day
1	1
2	4
3	9
4	16

How many repetitions will Kendra do on day 8 of this plan? _____

TOPIC 2

> **How do you know?**

_____

_____

_____

_____

_____

_____

_____

_____

TOPIC 1

SCORE ⓪ ① ②   0 = Incorrect or No Response
1 = Partial Response
2 = Complete and Accurate

PERFORMANCE TASK

> **YOUR JOB**
> Fitness Trainer

> **YOUR TASK**
> Help your clients to reach their personal fitness goals.

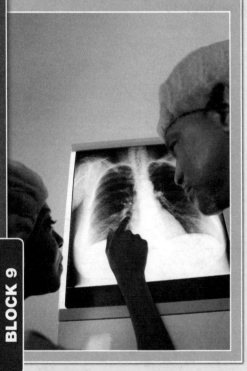

ANCHOR VIDEO CONNECTION

As the Anchor Video shows, comparing linear functions with different initial values and variables helps people pick the best medical option.

Analyze Fitness Plans

> You have two clients who are training to pass the military fitness exam. The three standard levels for graduation—Liberator, Thunderbolt, and Warhawk—are shown in the table. Each requires a different amount of sit-ups. Help your clients determine if they will reach the graduation standards with their plans.

A EXPLORE

Use the information to write equations expressing the number of sit-ups Jamal and Cindy will be able to do over time.

Graduation Standard Levels	Number of Sit-Ups	
	Male	Female
Liberator (minimum)	50	50
Thunderbolt (honor)	70	60
Warhawk (extraordinary)	80	75

Variables:

x represents the _____

y represents the _____

Jamal's Plan

Jamal can do 30 sit-ups. He plans to increase the number of sit-ups by 2 each day.

Jamal's equation: _____

Cindy's Plan

Cindy can do 20 sit-ups. She plans to increase the number of sit-ups by 4 each day.

Cindy's equation: _____

B APPLY

Graph and label the equations you wrote for Jamal and Cindy. Use the graph or equations to answer the questions and fill in the blanks.

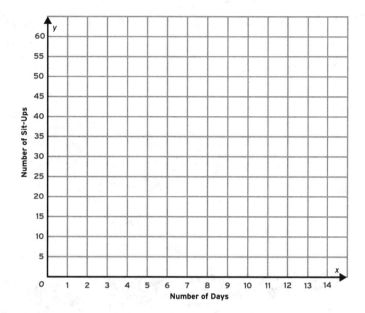

1. Who has the higher initial value? _____

2. Who has the higher rate of change? _____

3. Jamal and Cindy will do the same number of sit-ups at _____ days.

4. Who will meet the Liberator standard first? _____

5. Jamal will reach the Liberator standard at _____ days.

C ANALYZE

EXPLAIN The test is in 10 days. Which standards will Jamal and Cindy reach?

_____

_____

_____

REFLECT Jamal wants to reach the Warhawk standard in 10 days. Recommend a change to his plan.

_____

_____

_____

> Rate how well you and your partner understood and completed each part of the performance task.

Ranking Scale			
None	Limited	Partial	Thorough
0	1	2	3

A Wrote accurate equations for Jamal and Cindy.

Me	0	1	2	3
Partner	0	1	2	3

B Correctly graphed the equations and answered all questions.

Me	0	1	2	3
Partner	0	1	2	3

C Answered each question thoughtfully.

Me	0	1	2	3
Partner	0	1	2	3

EXTEND

Cindy also wants to reach the Warhawk standard. At her current rate, how many more days does Cindy need to train?

_____

_____

_____

_____

_____

_____

BLOCK 9 · MINDSET STRATEGY

Reflect on Overcoming Obstacles
Congratulations! You've completed Block 9 of *MATH 180*.

Reaching for the Stars

As a child, Candy Torres dreamed of joining NASA's space program, but family and friends told her that Latinas were not meant to have those types of careers. In the 1970s, there were few women or minority students in the space program.

Never Give Up

Torres began to doubt herself, but she knew she was the only person who could make her dreams a reality. "I always knew that if I wanted to reach my goals, I was going to have to work hard and never quit," she said in an interview with CNN.

Making Dreams a Reality

Candy Torres never gave up, and in 1976, she earned a degree in space science from Rutgers University. The very next day, she was offered a job working on a space project at Princeton University and later volunteered at NASA's International Space Station.

> **"It's not necessarily other people that are going to keep you from doing what you're going to do—it's yourself."**
>
> —Candy Torres, on Latino USA

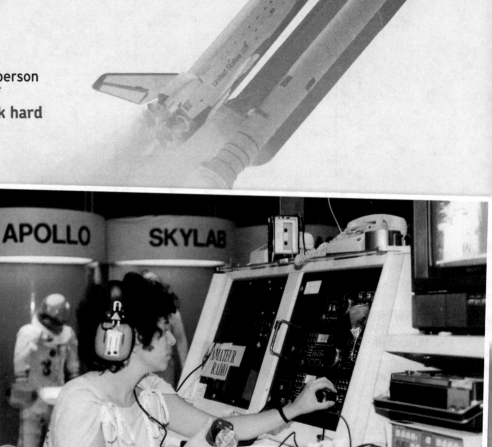

Candy Torres, coding at NASA Johnson Space Center early in her career

Overcoming Obstacles

> Reframing challenges is a good way to start to overcome tough obstacles.

Reframe it: Under stress, people often have a "fight-or-flight" reaction. Their heart rate goes up, and they feel sweaty, shaky, or distracted. This is how your body gets ready for a challenge. Fight negative feelings by reframing negative thoughts into positive, growth-minded language.

NEGATIVE THOUGHTS	REFRAME
"This is too hard."	I can learn from this.
"This kind of work isn't for me."	
"I might fail at this."	

Your Dream Career

> Imagine you are working hard to land the career of your dreams, just like Candy Torres.

> What is the career of your dreams?

_____

_____

> List two obstacles that you might face in working toward your dream job.

1. _____

_____

2. _____

_____

_____

> What negative thoughts might you face, and how can you reframe them?

NEGATIVE THOUGHTS	REFRAME

Table of Contents

Multiplication Facts 224

Problem-Solving Routine 225

Symbols 226

Measurement 228

Properties 230

Visual Models 232

Talking About Math 234

Multiplication Facts

> Use this chart to help you remember multiplication facts.

✕	0	1	2	3	4	5	6	7	8	9	10	11	12
0	0	0	0	0	0	0	0	0	0	0	0	0	0
1	0	1	2	3	4	5	6	7	8	9	10	11	12
2	0	2	4	6	8	10	12	14	16	18	20	22	24
3	0	3	6	9	12	15	18	21	24	27	30	33	36
4	0	4	8	12	16	20	24	28	32	36	40	44	48
5	0	5	10	15	20	25	30	35	40	45	50	55	60
6	0	6	12	18	24	30	36	42	48	54	60	66	72
7	0	7	14	21	28	35	42	49	56	63	70	77	84
8	0	8	16	24	32	40	48	56	64	72	80	88	96
9	0	9	18	27	36	45	54	63	72	81	90	99	108
10	0	10	20	30	40	50	60	70	80	90	100	110	120
11	0	11	22	33	44	55	66	77	88	99	110	121	132
12	0	12	24	36	48	60	72	84	96	108	120	132	144

> **Use this routine to help you analyze and solve word problems.**

STEPS	WHAT TO DO	EXAMPLE
Read It! **Read the problem.**	■ Read and make sense of the problem. ■ Ask yourself, "What is the problem asking me to find? What should I do first?"	*MUSIC SALES ANALYST* The sales trend of two albums is 1:2. A store sells 100 copies of album A. Based on this trend, how many copies of album A and album B will the store sell altogether?
Show It! **Represent the problem.**	■ Use a visual model to represent the information in the problem. ■ Remember to label all the quantities correctly.	<table><tr><td>Album A</td><td>Album B</td></tr><tr><td>1</td><td>2</td></tr><tr><td>100</td><td>200</td></tr></table> x 100 … x 100
Solve It! **Solve the problem.**	■ Write an equation or equations to represent the solution. ■ Solve the problem.	$100 + 200 = 300$ The store sells <u>300</u> albums altogether.
Check It! **Check your work.**	■ Check your work carefully. ■ You may want to use a different strategy to solve the problem. ■ Ask yourself, "Is my answer reasonable?"	$1 + 2 = 3$ $3 \times 100 = 300$ **My answer is reasonable because** when I multiply the sum of the values in the first ratio by 100, I get the sum of the values in the second ratio.

> **Mathematicians use symbols to show relationships between numbers.**

SYMBOL	EXAMPLE	MEANING	SYMBOL	EXAMPLE	MEANING
$+$	$56.01 + 0.6$	plus or add	$=$	$0.5 = \frac{1}{2}$ $y = 2x$	is equal to
$-$	$\frac{3}{4} - \frac{1}{4}$	minus or subtract	$\neq$	$\frac{1}{10} \neq 0.01$	is not equal to
$\times$	180×4	times or multiply	$\approx$	$1.978 \approx 2$	is approximately equal to
$\cdot$	$3 \cdot 2$	times or multiply	$<$	$40 < 400$	is less than
$\div$	$14 \div 7$	divide	$\leq$	$-0.546 \leq -0.545$	is less than or equal to
$\overline{)}$	$7\overline{)14}$	divide	$>$	$16 > 1.6$	is greater than
$-$	$\frac{14}{7}$	divide	$\geq$	$0.546 \geq 0.545$	is greater than or equal to

SYMBOL	EXAMPLE	MEANING
...	0.333333...	continues without end
+	+4	positive
−	−5	negative
( )	$10 \div (2 + 3) = 2$ $5(x + 2) = 5x + 10$ $(3, -2)$	evaluate first multiply ordered pair
{ }	{0, 1, 2, 3, 4}	shows members of a set
a^b	$2^3 = 2 \cdot 2 \cdot 2$ $= 8$	raise to a power
%	25%	per 100
.	3.5	decimal point

SYMBOL	EXAMPLE	MEANING
| |	|−10| = 10	absolute value
°	45°	degrees
Δ	ΔABC	triangle
~	$\Delta ABC \sim \Delta DEF$	is similar to
π	$\pi \approx 3.1415927$	ratio of circumference to diameter
—	$\frac{3}{11} = 0.27272...$ $= 0.\overline{27}$	repeating decimal
:	3:2	ratio
$\sqrt{\ }$	$\sqrt{9} = \sqrt{3^2}$ $= 3$	square root

> Knowing how measurements relate to each other helps you solve problems.

CONVERSIONS

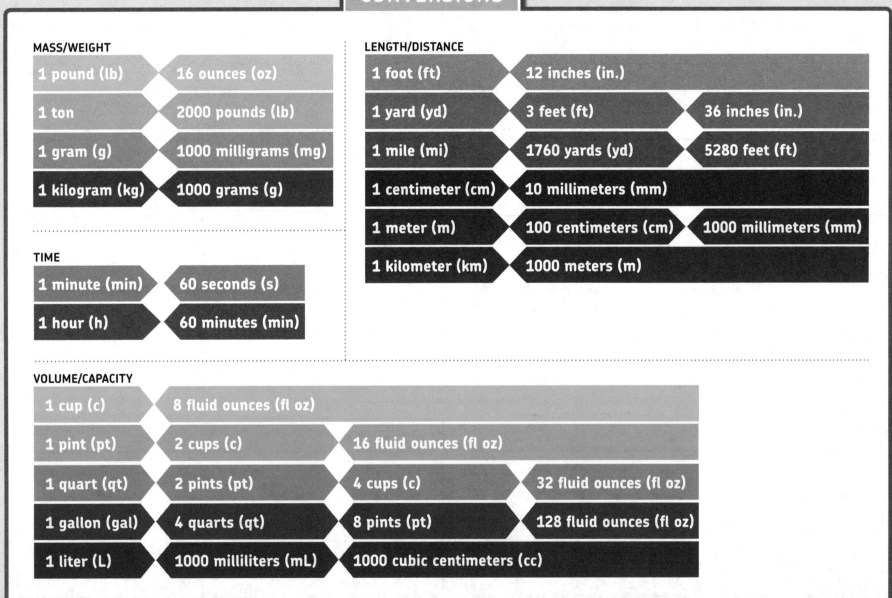

MASS/WEIGHT

1 pound (lb)	16 ounces (oz)
1 ton	2000 pounds (lb)
1 gram (g)	1000 milligrams (mg)
1 kilogram (kg)	1000 grams (g)

TIME

| 1 minute (min) | 60 seconds (s) |
| 1 hour (h) | 60 minutes (min) |

LENGTH/DISTANCE

1 foot (ft)	12 inches (in.)	
1 yard (yd)	3 feet (ft)	36 inches (in.)
1 mile (mi)	1760 yards (yd)	5280 feet (ft)
1 centimeter (cm)	10 millimeters (mm)	
1 meter (m)	100 centimeters (cm)	1000 millimeters (mm)
1 kilometer (km)	1000 meters (m)	

VOLUME/CAPACITY

1 cup (c)	8 fluid ounces (fl oz)		
1 pint (pt)	2 cups (c)	16 fluid ounces (fl oz)	
1 quart (qt)	2 pints (pt)	4 cups (c)	32 fluid ounces (fl oz)
1 gallon (gal)	4 quarts (qt)	8 pints (pt)	128 fluid ounces (fl oz)
1 liter (L)	1000 milliliters (mL)	1000 cubic centimeters (cc)	

PERIMETER

rectangle	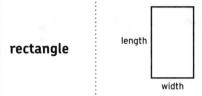 length / width	$P = 2l + 2w$ $P = 2(l + w)$
circle	circumference / diameter / radius	$C = 2\pi r$ $C = \pi d$

AREA

triangle	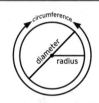 height / base	$A = \frac{1}{2}bh$
rectangle	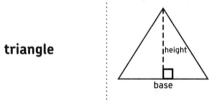 length / width	$A = lw$
circle	radius	$A = \pi r^2$

VOLUME

rectangular prism	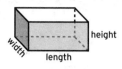 width / height / length	$V = lwh$
cylinder	height / radius	$V = \pi r^2 h$

SLOPE

slope of a line	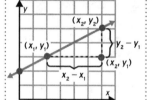	$m = \dfrac{y_2 - y_1}{x_2 - x_1}$
slope-intercept form of the equation of a line	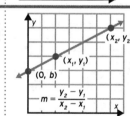	$y = mx + b$

ALGEBRA

Pythagorean Theorem	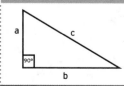 a / c / 90° / b	$a^2 + b^2 = c^2$
distance	150 miles = 50 miles per hour × 3 hours	$d = rt$

> In mathematics, a property is a characteristic of an operation, a number, or an equality.

THE ASSOCIATIVE PROPERTY

PROPERTY	MEANING	EXAMPLE
Associative Property of Addition	The way we group three or more addends doesn't change the sum.	$(3 + 4) + 5 = 3 + (4 + 5)$ $7 + 5 = 3 + 9$ $12 = 12$
Associative Property of Multiplication	The way we group three or more factors doesn't change the product.	$(2 \times 3) \times 4 = 2 \times (3 \times 4)$ $6 \times 4 = 2 \times 12$ $24 = 24$

THE COMMUTATIVE PROPERTY

PROPERTY	MEANING	EXAMPLE
Commutative Property of Addition	Changing the order of the addends does not change the sum.	$4 + 3 = 3 + 4$ $7 = 7$
Commutative Property of Multiplication	Changing the order of the factors does not change the product.	$4 \times 3 = 3 \times 4$ $12 = 12$

THE DISTRIBUTIVE PROPERTY

PROPERTY	MEANING	EXAMPLE
Distributive Property of Multiplication	Multiplying a sum by a number is the same as adding the partial products.	$8 \times 24 = 8 \times (20 + 4)$ $= (8 \times 20) + (8 \times 4)$ $= 160 + 32$ $= 192$

THE IDENTITY PROPERTY

PROPERTY	MEANING	EXAMPLE
Additive Identity Property	Adding 0 to a number does not change the number's value.	$4 + 0 = 4$ or $0 + 4 = 4$
Multiplicative Identity Property	Multiplying a number by 1 does not change the number's value.	$7 \times 1 = 7$ or $1 \times 7 = 7$

THE INVERSE PROPERTY

PROPERTY	MEANING	EXAMPLE
Inverse Property of Addition	Adding a number to its opposite results in a sum of 0.	$5 + (-5) = 0$ or $(-5) + 5 = 0$
Inverse Property of Multiplication	Multiplying a number (excluding 0) by its reciprocal results in a product of 1.	$4 \times \frac{1}{4} = 1$ or $(-\frac{1}{4}) \times (-4) = 1$

THE ZERO PROPERTY

PROPERTY	MEANING	EXAMPLE
Zero Property of Multiplication	Multiplying a number by 0 results in a product of 0.	$8 \cdot 0 = 0$ or $0 \cdot x = 0$

PROPERTIES OF EQUALITY

PROPERTY	MEANING	EXAMPLE
Addition Property of Equality	Adding the same number to both sides of an equation preserves equality.	If $y = 2x$, then $y + 5 = 2x + 5$.
Multiplication Property of Equality	Multiplying both sides of an equation by the same number preserves equality.	If $y = x + 2$, then $5y = 5(x + 2)$.
Substitution Property of Equality	If two expressions are equal, then one may be substituted for the other in any expression or equation.	If $x = 2$ and $y = x + 7$, then $y = 2 + 7$ and $y = 9$.

Visual Models

> **Visual models are helpful tools for representing and solving problems.**

GRAPH

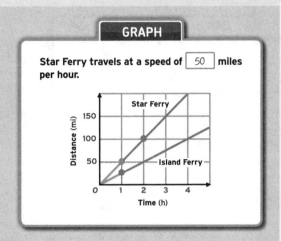

Star Ferry travels at a speed of 50 miles per hour.

MOTION MODEL

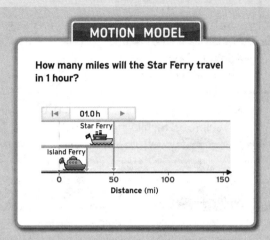

How many miles will the Star Ferry travel in 1 hour?

TABLE

The ferries travel at constant rates. Write the missing value in the table.

Time (h)	Distance (mi)	
	Star Ferry	Island Ferry
0	0	0
1	50	25
2	100	50

WHAT IS IT?

A diagram, defined by a horizontal axis and a vertical axis, that shows relationships between quantities as sets of points

An interactive model that shows the motion of objects over time

A set of numbers arranged in rows and columns, usually with a header row that describes each column

---

WHY USE IT?

Use the **Graph** to...
- plot points or ordered pairs
- graph functions
- analyze relationships

Use the **Motion Model** to...
- investigate one-dimensional motion
- understand relationships between distance and time

Use the **Table** to...
- organize data
- analyze relationships between related quantities
- generate equivalent ratios

BAR MODEL	DOUBLE NUMBER LINE	DECIMAL GRID

BAR MODEL

The ratio of paper to plastic recycling bins is 2:3. There are 8 bins for paper. How many bins are there for plastic?

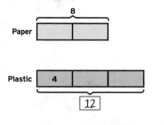

DOUBLE NUMBER LINE

José has a 20% discount at a gaming store. A new video game costs $60. How much does José pay for the video game?

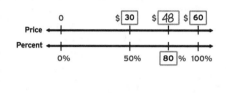

DECIMAL GRID

$$\frac{3}{5} = \frac{60}{100} = 0.60 = 60\%$$

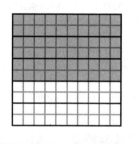

WHAT IS IT?

An interactive model that uses equal-sized units to model proportional relationships between related quantities

A pair of connected parallel number lines that shows how two measures of the same quantity vary together

A 10 x 10 array of squares, partially shaded to indicate equivalent forms of rational numbers between 0 and 1

WHY USE IT?

Use the **Bar Model** to. . .
- represent and solve problems with unknown quantities
- represent part-part and part-whole ratios

Use the **Double Number Line** to. . .
- show equivalence between numbers in fraction, decimal, and percent forms
- represent and solve percent problems

Use the **Decimal Grid** to. . .
- represent fraction, decimal, and percent forms of rational numbers
- convert between forms of rational numbers

> Use clear mathematical language to talk about math problems and concepts.

ANALYZE

- This problem is asking me to _____.
- The quantities in this problem are _____. They are related because _____.
- I already know that _____.

REASON

- I agree/disagree with _____ that _____ because _____.
- My idea builds upon _____'s because _____.
- When is _____ always/sometimes/never true?

I agree with Juan that order doesn't matter when multiplying two factors because multiplying 9 × 7 and 7 × 9 results in the same product: 63.

CONTEXTUALIZE

- A real-life example of _____ is _____.
- I used _____ to represent _____ because _____.
- How could you represent _____ with numbers?

EVALUATE

- One tool I can use to help me is _____ because _____.
- What is another strategy for _____?
- When I compare my result with my prediction, I find that _____.

The value of the quotient of 400 ÷ 5 can't be 8 because when I multiply to check my work, I see that 8 × 5 is 40.

IDENTIFY

- The value can/can't be _____ because _____ .
- I can find _____ by _____ because _____.
- What is the relationship between/among _____?

When I compare my result with my prediction, I find that the answer of 70% is close to my estimate of 75%. So, my answer is reasonable.

I figured out what the problem is asking me to do by drawing a bar model to show that the hybrid car travels 50 miles on each gallon of gas .

INFER

- I tried _____ and found out _____. Then I tried _____.
  - I figured out what the problem is asking me to do by _____.
  - What's another way to _____?

JUSTIFY

- I used the strategy of _____ because _____.
- Another example of _____ is _____.
- Does _____ still work if you _____?

I can represent the problem by labeling the percent and the whole on a double number line because it shows that I need to find the part .

REPRESENT

- I can represent the problem by _____ because _____.
- I can conclude that _____ because I know _____.
- The result makes sense because _____.

DEFINE

- I know the value _____ is appropriate for this situation because _____.
- The term/symbol _____ means _____.
- Can you explain how to _____?

GENERALIZE

- If _____, then the result will be _____ because _____.
- I notice that _____ will/won't always work because _____.
- _____ is a reasonable answer because _____.

If you multiply two unit fractions, then the product will be less than both fractions because the denominator will be greater, resulting in a smaller fraction .

MATH TERMS

MATH TERM	MEANING	EXAMPLE
A		
Addition Property of Equality (noun)	Adding the same number to both sides of an *equation* preserves equality.	If $y = 2x$, then $y + 5 = 2x + 5$.
Additive Identity Property (noun)	Adding 0 to a number does not change the number's *value*.	$4 + 0 = 4$ or $0 + 4 = 4$
additive inverse (noun)	The number we add to another number to get a *sum* of 0. The additive inverse of a number is also known as its opposite. (see *inverse operation*)	$-4 + ④ = 0$ additive inverse of -4
algebraic expression (noun)	An *expression* with a *variable*.	$8p$ $x + 3$ $2(a - b)$
approximately equal (adjective)	Not exactly *equal*, but close in *value*. The *symbol* ≈ represents "approximately equal to." (see *representation*)	$\pi \approx 3.14$ $\$2.99 \approx \$3.00$
area (noun)	The measure of the amount of space inside a flat figure; area is measured in square units; the *formula* for the area of a rectangle is $A = lw$, where l and w represent the length and width. (see *unit*, *volume*)	$A = 5 \times 7$ The area of the rectangle is 35 square units. 7 5
Associative Property of Addition (noun)	The way we group three or more addends doesn't change their *sum*.	$(3 + 4) + 5 = 3 + (4 + 5)$ $7 + 5 = 3 + 9$ $12 = 12$

MATH TERM	MEANING	EXAMPLE
Associative Property of Multiplication (noun)	The way we group three or more factors doesn't change their *product*. (see *factor*)	$(2 \times 3) \times 4 = 2 \times (3 \times 4)$ $6 \times 4 = 2 \times 12$ $24 = 24$
B		
base (noun)	A number or *expression* that is used as a *factor* more than once. (see *exponent*)	$②^3 = 2 \cdot 2 \cdot 2 = 8$ base
benchmark (noun)	A familiar number that we use to make a comparison or an *estimate*.	
C		
coefficient (noun)	A number multiplied by a *variable* in an *algebraic expression*. (see *multiply*)	$③x + ⑦y$ coefficients
collinear points (noun)	Points that lie on the same *line*. (see *point*)	
Commutative Property of Addition (noun)	Changing the order of addends does not change their *sum*.	$4 + 3 = 3 + 4$ $7 = 7$
Commutative Property of Multiplication (noun)	Changing the order of factors does not change their *product*. (see *factor*)	$4 \times 3 = 3 \times 4$ $12 = 12$

MATH TERM	MEANING	EXAMPLE
constant *(adjective)*	Not changing.	The train traveled at a constant speed.
constant *(noun)*	A *value* that does not vary; a fixed *quantity*. (see *variable*)	The numbers 0, 1, −5, 0.5, and $\frac{1}{3}$ are constants.
constant of proportionality *(noun)*	The unchanging *ratio* between two quantities in a *proportional relationship*; often the *k* in *y* = *kx*. (see *constant*, *quantity*)	Ella earned $18 per hour.
constant rate *(noun)*	A *rate* that does not change or vary. (see *constant*)	
constant term *(noun)*	In an *algebraic expression*, a number that is not multiplied by a *variable*. (see *constant*)	$3x + ⑥$ constant term
coordinate *(noun)*	Either number in an *ordered pair* that gives the location of a *point*, relative to the *origin* (0, 0), on a *coordinate plane*.	

MATH TERM	MEANING	EXAMPLE
coordinate plane *(noun)*	The 2-dimensional plane defined by the *intersection*, at (0, 0), of two perpendicular axes. Every *point* on the coordinate plane can be located by an *ordered pair*. (see *coordinate*, *horizontal axis*, *vertical axis*)	

D

MATH TERM	MEANING	EXAMPLE
data *(noun)*	A set of collected information or facts used to analyze, plan, or calculate. Data are often represented in a *table* or a *graph*.	
decimal *(noun)*	A number with digits arranged by place *value*; we usually refer to a number as a decimal only if there is a *decimal point* followed by digits.	2654.387 *decimal*
decimal point *(noun)*	The *symbol* (dot or period) used to separate the whole-number *part* from the fractional *part* in a *decimal*.	0.8 *decimal point*
denominator *(noun)*	The number below the *fraction* bar in a *fraction*. It tells the number of parts in one *whole*. (see *part*)	$\frac{3}{④}$ *denominator*

MATH TERM	MEANING	EXAMPLE
difference *(noun)*	The result of subtraction. (see *plot*)	$5 - 1 = ④$ *difference*
distance *(noun)*	The measure of the length between two points, often on a *number line* or on a *coordinate plane*. (see *point*)	
Distributive Property *(noun)*	Multiplying a *sum* by a number is the same as adding the *partial products*. (see *multiply*)	$8 \times 24 = 8 \times (20 + 4)$ $= (8 \times 20) + (8 \times 4)$ $= \ \ 160 \ \ + \ \ 32$ $= \ \ 192$
divide *(verb)*	To split into *equal* parts or groups. (see *division, part*)	$6\overline{)24}\,^{4}$ $24 \div 6 = 4$ $\frac{24}{6} = 4$
division *(noun)*	The *operation* of creating *equal* parts from a number or creating *equal* groups in a set. (see *divide, part*)	$6\overline{)24}\,^{4}$ $24 \div 6 = 4$ $\frac{24}{6} = 4$

E

MATH TERM	MEANING	EXAMPLE
equal *(adjective)*	Having the same amount or *value*. (see *equation, inequality*)	$11 + 7 = 18$ 60 seconds = 1 minute 1 dollar = 100 cents

MATH TERM	MEANING	EXAMPLE
equation *(noun)*	A mathematical sentence that states that two quantities or expressions are *equal*. (see *equivalent, expression, quantity*)	$3.5 = 4 - \frac{1}{2}$ $d = 8t$ $y = 5x$
equivalent *(adjective)*	Having the same meaning or having the same *value*.	5×4 is equivalent to 5 groups of 4. 5×4 is equivalent to $10 + 10$. 5×4 is equivalent to 2×10.
equivalent fractions *(noun)*	Two or more fractions that name the same *part* of a *whole*. (see *equivalent, fraction, simplest form*)	 $\frac{3}{4} = \frac{6}{8}$
equivalent ratios *(noun)*	Two or more ratios that have the same *value*. (see *equivalent, ratio, simplest form*)	 2:4, 20:40, and 3:6 are equivalent ratios.
estimate *(noun)*	An approximate calculation often based on rounding or using benchmarks or compatible numbers. A good estimate is close to the exact answer. (see *approximately equal, benchmark*)	A good estimate of 1584×1024 can be found by first rounding each factor to the nearest hundred, and then multiplying. $1600 \times 1000 = 1,600,000$
estimate *(verb)*	To approximate a calculation by rounding or using benchmarks or compatible numbers. (see *approximately equal, benchmark*)	We can estimate the value of 1584×1024 by first rounding each factor to the nearest hundred and then multiplying. $1600 \times 1000 = 1,600,000$

MATH TERM	MEANING	EXAMPLE
evaluate *(verb)*	To find the *value* of an *expression*, often after substitution. (see *substitute*)	Evaluate 100 ÷ x when x = 20. 100 ÷ 20 = 5
exponent *(noun)*	The number of times a number (the *base*) is used as a *factor* in the same *term*.	exponent $2^3 = 2 \cdot 2 \cdot 2 = 8$
expression *(noun)*	A *representation* of a number or *quantity* using variables, constants, and/or *operation* symbols. (see *constant, symbol, variable*)	$2n + 4$ $\frac{1}{8} \times 5 \times 3$ $-3 - 7$ $x^2 + 2x$ 0
factor *(noun)*	One of at least two numbers we *multiply* to find a *product*.	$4 \times 5 = 20$ factors
formula *(noun)*	A general rule that shows a relationship among variables in which the *value* of one *variable* is dependent on the values of other variables. (see *area, volume*)	length width $A = lw$
fraction *(noun)*	A number that names *equal* parts of a *whole* or *equal* parts of a set. (see *denominator, numerator, part*)	$\frac{1}{4}$ of a whole $\frac{1}{4}$ of a set

MATH TERM	MEANING	EXAMPLE
function *(noun)*	A set of ordered pairs for which each *input* has exactly one *output*. A function can be thought of as a rule: given each *input*, we apply the rule to determine the corresponding unique *output*. (see *ordered pair*)	function $y = 0.5x + 1$ input x = 1 → 0.5(1) + 1 = 1.5 → output y = 1.5 ordered pair (1, 1.5)
graph *(noun)*	The *representation*, in the *coordinate plane*, of the ordered pairs that make an *equation* with two variables true. (see *ordered pair, variable*)	graph of y = 1.5x
greater than *(adjective)*	Having a *value* plotted farther to the right on a *number line*; the symbol > expresses that one *quantity* is greater than another *quantity*, where the open side of the symbol faces the greater *quantity*. (see *less than*)	10 > 8 10 is greater than 8.
horizontal axis *(noun)*	A *line* on the *coordinate plane* that runs straight across the *origin*, left and right, often called the x-axis. Every *point* on the x-axis has a y-coordinate of 0. (see *vertical axis*)	horizontal axis

For the function table:

Input x	function y = 0.5x + 1	output y	ordered pair
−2	0.5(−2) + 1	0	(−2, 0)
0	0.5(0) + 1	1	(0, 1)
1	0.5(1) + 1	1.5	(1, 1.5)
2	0.5(2) + 1	2	(2, 2)
4	0.5(4) + 1	3	(4, 3)

MATH TERMS

MATH TERM	MEANING	EXAMPLE
inequality *(noun)*	A mathematical sentence that shows that two expressions are not *equal* or might not be *equal*. The symbols < (*less than*), ≤ (*less than* or *equal* to), > (*greater than*), ≥ (*greater than* or *equal* to), and ≠ (not *equal* to), can be placed between two expressions to show their relationship. (see *equation, expression, symbol*)	$1 + 4 < 6$ $x \leq 8$ $-5 - 5 > -11$ $y \geq 0$ $x + 1 \neq x$
initial value *(noun)*	The starting or first *value* of a *function*; often the *value* of y when $x = 0$. Not all functions have initial values. (see *y-intercept*)	
input *(noun)*	A *value* we *substitute* for a *variable* in a *function* to determine a corresponding unique *output*. When y is a *function* of x, x is the input and y is the output.	
integers *(noun)*	*Whole numbers*, their opposites, and zero. (see *additive inverse*)	$\ldots -5, -4, -3, -2, -1, 0, 1, 2, 3, 4, 5, \ldots$

MATH TERM	MEANING	EXAMPLE
intersection *(noun)*	A *point* at which two graphs or grid lines meet. The intersection of two *linear* graphs represents the *solution* to the *linear* system of their equations. (see *coordinate plane, equation, graph, line, linear equation, representation, satisfy, system of equations*)	
interval *(noun)*	All the points, on a *line*, between and possibly including either or both of two *segment* endpoints. On a *number line*, intervals between consecutive tick marks are of *equal* length. (see *point, representation*)	
inverse operation *(noun)*	An *operation* that reverses or inverts the effect of another *operation*. (see *additive inverse, Inverse Property of Addition, Inverse Property of Multiplication, multiplicative inverse*)	Addition and subtraction are inverse operations. $3 + 4 = 7$ $7 - 4 = 3$ Multiplication and division are inverse operations. $3 \times 4 = 12$ $12 \div 4 = 3$
Inverse Property of Addition *(noun)*	Adding a number to its *opposite* (*additive inverse*) results in a *sum* of 0.	$5 + (-5) = 0$ and $(-5) + 5 = 0$

MATH TERM	MEANING	EXAMPLE
Inverse Property of Multiplication *(noun)*	Multiplying a non-zero number by its reciprocal (*multiplicative inverse*) results in a *product* of 1. (see *inverse operation, multiply*)	$4 \times \frac{1}{4} = 1$ or $\left(-\frac{1}{4}\right) \times (-4) = 1$
irrational number *(noun)*	A number that cannot be expressed as a *ratio* of two *integers*. The *decimal* form of an irrational number does not terminate or repeat. (see *expression*)	$\pi = 3.1415927\ldots$ $\sqrt{2} = 1.414213562\ldots$ $\frac{\sqrt{3}}{2} = 0.8660\ldots$
less than *(adjective)*	Having a *value* plotted farther to the left on a *number line*; the *symbol* < expresses that one *quantity* is less than another *quantity*, where the closed side of the *symbol* points to the lesser *quantity*. (see *greater than*)	$-5 < -3$ -5 is less than -3.
line *(noun)*	A straight, connected set of points extending in two directions with no end. (see *coordinate plane, graph, point*)	
linear *(adjective)*	Relating to or forming a *line*; an *equation* or *function* is linear if its *graph* is a straight *line*. (see *collinear, linear equation, nonlinear*)	$F = 1.8C + 32$

MATH TERM	MEANING	EXAMPLE
linear equation *(noun)*	An *equation* whose *graph* is a *line*. (see *coordinate plane*)	$y = -x + \frac{3}{2}$ linear equation
line of symmetry *(noun)*	A *line* that divides a plane figure or *graph* into two identical parts, each the mirror image of the other. (see *symmetry*)	line of symmetry
mixed number *(noun)*	A number *greater than* 1 that includes both an integer *part* and a fractional *part*. (see *integers, fraction*)	$1\frac{57}{100}$ $3\frac{4}{5}$
model *(noun)*	A mathematical *representation* of a mathematical or real-world situation, often in the form of an *equation* or drawing.	Podcasts Songs $\frac{1}{5}$ $\frac{3}{5}$

MATH TERM	MEANING	EXAMPLE
model (verb)	To represent a mathematical or real-world situation (with a *number line, graph, equation,* bar *model,* or other form). (see *representation*)	 $400
motion (noun)	Change in position or *distance* of an object compared to time and a starting *point*.	 The car travels 12 meters in __3__ seconds.
multiple (noun)	A *product* of a given number and a *positive* integer. (see *integers*)	multiples of 5: _5, 10, 15, 20, 25, ..._
multiplication (noun)	The repeated addition of a number a certain number of times. Multiplication can involve factors that are not *integers*, as when finding the *area* of a rectangle. (see *factor*)	$3 \times 6 = 18$ 3 equal groups of 6 is 18. Area = 1.5 m × 2.6 m = 3.9 m²
Multiplication Property of Equality (noun)	Multiplying both sides of an *equation* by the same number preserves equality. (see *equal, multiplication, multiply*)	If $y = x + 2$, then $5y = 5(x + 2)$.

MATH TERM	MEANING	EXAMPLE
multiplicative (adjective)	Having to do with *multiplication*. (see *multiply*)	 $5 \times \underline{50} = 250$ $15 \times \underline{50} = 750$ Fuel and distance are in a multiplicative relationship.
Multiplicative Identity Property (noun)	Multiplying a number by 1 does not change the number's *value*. (see *multiplication*)	$4 \times 1 = 4$ or $1 \times 4 = 4$
multiplicative inverse (noun)	The number we *multiply* by another number to get a *product* of 1. The *multiplicative* inverse of a number is also known as its reciprocal. (see *multiplication*)	multiplicative inverse of 6 $6 \times \frac{1}{6} = \frac{6}{6}$ $= 1$ multiplicative inverse of $\frac{3}{4}$ $\frac{3}{4} \times \frac{4}{3} = \frac{12}{12}$ $= 1$
multiplier (noun)	The number we *multiply* by; the *factor* that is used to find an *equivalent ratio*. (see *equivalent ratios*)	
multiply (verb)	To determine the total number of objects in *equal* groups. We can multiply factors that are not *integers*, as when we find the *area* of a rectangle. (see *factor, multiplication*)	5 groups of 2 $5 \times 2 = 10$ 3 groups of $\frac{1}{2}$ $3 \times \frac{1}{2} = \frac{3}{2}$

MATH TERM	MEANING	EXAMPLE
N		
negative (adjective)	Having a *value* graphed on the left side of 0 on a horizontal *number line*; *less than* 0. (see *positive*)	negative
nonlinear (adjective)	Not forming a *line*; an *equation* or *function* is nonlinear if its *graph* is not a straight *line*. (see *collinear, linear*)	$y = x^2$
number line (noun)	A *line* on which every *point* names one number and every number has a unique location.	
numerator (noun)	The number above the *fraction* bar in a *fraction*. It tells the number of *equal* parts being described. (see *part*)	numerator $\dfrac{3}{4}$
O		
operation (noun)	A mathematical process defined by a rule and performed on one or more numbers to get a resulting number; the most common operations are addition, subtraction, *multiplication*, and *division*.	$24 \div 6 = 4$ $10.12 + 9.22 = 19.34$ operations

MATH TERM	MEANING	EXAMPLE
order of operations (noun)	The sequence in which operations are performed to *evaluate* an *expression*. ( ) Perform operations within parentheses and other grouping symbols. x^2 Evaluate exponential expressions. ×, ÷ *Multiply* and *divide* from left to right. +, − Add and subtract from left to right. (see *exponent, expression, operation, symbol*)	$3(4.5 + 1.5) - 6(-2)^2$ $= 3 \cdot 6 - 6(-2)^2$ $= 3 \cdot 6 - 6 \cdot 4$ $= 18 - 24$ $= 18 + (-24)$ $= -6$
ordered pair (noun)	Two numbers, often (x, y), used to locate the position of a *point* on a *coordinate plane*. The first number tells the left or right *distance* from the *vertical axis*. The second number tells the up or down *distance* from the *horizontal axis*. (see *coordinate*)	
origin (noun)	The *point* in the *coordinate plane* where the *x*-axis and *y*-axis intersect. The origin has coordinates (0, 0). (see *coordinate, horizontal axis, vertical axis*)	origin (0, 0)

MATH TERM	MEANING	EXAMPLE
output *(noun)*	The result of applying a *function* rule to an *input*. When y is a *function* of x, x is the *input* and y is the output.	function $y = 0.5x + 1$ input $x = 1$ → $0.5(1) + 1 = 1.5$ → output $y = 1.5$ ordered pair (1, 1.5) <table><tr><th>input x</th><th>function $y = 0.5x + 1$</th><th>output y</th><th>ordered pair</th></tr><tr><td>−2</td><td>0.5(−2) + 1</td><td>0</td><td>(−2, 0)</td></tr><tr><td>0</td><td>0.5(0) + 1</td><td>1</td><td>(0, 1)</td></tr><tr><td>1</td><td>0.5(1) + 1</td><td>1.5</td><td>(1, 1.5)</td></tr><tr><td>2</td><td>0.5(2) + 1</td><td>2</td><td>(2, 2)</td></tr><tr><td>4</td><td>0.5(4) + 1</td><td>3</td><td>(4, 3)</td></tr></table>
parallel lines *(noun)*	Lines in a plane that never intersect or touch. Parallel lines in the *coordinate plane* have the same *slope*. (see *intersection*, *line*)	
part *(noun)*	A portion, or piece, of a *whole*. In a *percent* problem, the part is a *percent* of the whole.	part 225 315 450 People Percent 0% 50% 100%
partial products *(noun)*	Numbers you add when you break one of the factors into a *sum* of its parts to calculate a *product*. (see *Distributive Property*, *factor*, *multiplication*)	$8 \times 24 = 8 \times (20 + 4)$ $= (8 \times 20) + (8 \times 4)$ $= 160 + 32$ $= 192$ partial products

MATH TERM	MEANING	EXAMPLE
pattern *(noun)*	An ordered set of numbers or objects arranged in a way that follows a rule.	<table><tr><th>Point</th><th>Apples</th><th>Oranges</th></tr><tr><td>A</td><td>1</td><td>3</td></tr><tr><td>B</td><td>2</td><td>6</td></tr><tr><td>C</td><td>3</td><td>9</td></tr></table>
per *(preposition)*	For each. (see *rate*)	The cart travels __4__ meters in 1 second.
percent *(noun)*	A *rate* or *ratio per* 100. The % *symbol* is used to represent percent. A percent represents the size of the *part* relative to the *whole* (100%). (see *representation*)	Fraction: $\frac{23}{100}$ Decimal: 0.23 Percent: 23% 23% of the squares are shaded.
percent change *(noun)*	An increase or decrease expressed as a *percent*; tells how much a *quantity* has changed relative to the 100% it started as.	250 0% 20% 40% 60% 80% 100% 50 50 40% decrease

MATH TERM	MEANING	EXAMPLE
perfect square (noun)	The *square* of an integer; the *product* of an integer and itself. (see *integers*)	$1^2 = 1$ $7^2 = 49$ $2^2 = 4$ $8^2 = 64$ $3^2 = 9$ $9^2 = 81$ $4^2 = 16$ $10^2 = 100$ $5^2 = 25$ $11^2 = 121$ $6^2 = 36$ $12^2 = 144$ $3^2 = 9$
perimeter (noun)	The *distance* around a plane figure.	$P = 6 + 7 + 8 = 21$
plot (verb)	To represent a number with a *point* on a *number line*, or to represent an *ordered pair* of numbers with a *point* on a *coordinate plane*. (see *graph*, *representation*)	A (3, 1)
point (noun)	A location or position; the *intersection* of two distinct lines. A point has no length, width, or thickness. In the *coordinate plane*, a point is often named with an *ordered pair*. (see *coordinate*, *line*)	points

MATH TERM	MEANING	EXAMPLE
positive (adjective)	Having a *value* graphed on the right side of zero on a horizontal *number line*; *greater than* zero. (see *negative*)	positive
product (noun)	The result of *multiplication*. (see *multiply*, *operation*)	$4 \times 5 = 20$ $\frac{1}{2} \cdot (-3) = -\frac{3}{2}$ products
proportional relationship (noun)	A connection between two related quantities for which corresponding values form *equivalent ratios*. A proportional relationship can be represented by the *linear equation* $y = kx$. The *graph* of $y = kx$ includes the *origin*, (0, 0). (see *representation*, *quantity*, *value*)	**Feet** / **Inches**: 1 / 12; 2 / 24; 5 / 60. Feet and inches are in a proportional relationship because 1:12, 2:24, and 5:60 are equivalent ratios. $y = 12x$

Q

MATH TERM	MEANING	EXAMPLE
quadrant *(noun)*	One of the four sections into which the *coordinate plane* is divided by the *x*-axis and the *y*-axis. The four quadrants are usually named I, II, III, and IV. (see *divide, graph, horizontal axis, vertical axis*)	II (−,+) I (+,+) (0, 0) III (−,−) IV (+,−)
quadratic equation *(noun)*	An *equation* that results when a *quadratic function* is set *equal* to a *constant*, usually 0.	$x^2 - 4x + 3 = 0$
quadratic function *(noun)*	A quadratic *function* of a single *variable x* is a *function* for which the greatest *exponent* of *x* is 2. The *graph* of a quadratic *function* is a parabola.	$y = x^2 - 4x + 3$ is a quadratic function.
quantity *(noun)*	An amount that can be counted or measured; not a label. A varying quantity is often represented with a *variable*.	There are 54 students in Room 54. quantity label
quotient *(noun)*	The result of *division*.	quotient $24 \div 6 = 4$ $6\overline{)24}$ $\frac{24}{6} = 4$ quotient quotient

R

MATH TERM	MEANING	EXAMPLE
rate *(noun)*	A *multiplicative* comparison between two quantities measured in different units. (see *quantity, unit*)	Time (h) | Rate (mph) | Distance (mi) 1 | × 50 = | 50 2 | × 50 = | 100 6.3 | × 50 = | 315 50 miles per hour rate
rate of change *(noun)*	How fast one *quantity* changes with respect to another *quantity*. (see *rate*)	$F = 1.8C + 32$ $d = 55t$ Andrew drove at 55 miles per hour. rates of change
ratio *(noun)*	A *multiplicative* comparison of related numbers or quantities; often a *part* to a *part* of the same *whole*, a *part* to a *whole*, or a *whole* to a *part*. (see *quantity, rate*)	shaded : unshaded = 4:6 shaded : whole = 4:10 whole : unshaded = 10:6
ratio table *(noun)*	A *representation* of a *proportional relationship* between quantities, showing different yet *equivalent ratios*. Each *quantity is in a column*. Each *ratio is in a row*.	Point | Apples | Oranges A | 1 | 3 B | 2 | 6 C | 3 | 9
rational number *(noun)*	A number that can be expressed as the *quotient* of two *integers*, where the second integer does not *equal* zero. (see *expression, irrational number*)	$\frac{3}{5}$ $\frac{22}{7}$ −18 2.718 −3.14 $7\frac{2}{9}$

MATH TERM	MEANING	EXAMPLE
rectangle *(noun)*	A 4-sided closed plane figure with 4 right (90°) angles and opposite sides of *equal* length.	
reflection *(noun)*	A flip *transformation* over a *line of symmetry* or over a *point*. A reflection over a *line* looks like a mirror image. (see *symmetry*)	Reflection (over *y*-axis) Reflection (over origin)
representation *(noun)*	The mathematical form used; different representations can reveal different information about a math problem. A visual *model* used to understand a problem.	representations of the number 1.6: 1 + 0.6 one and six-tenths
right triangle *(noun)*	A triangle that has a right (90°) angle.	

MATH TERM	MEANING	EXAMPLE
rotation *(noun)*	A turn *transformation* around a *point*.	Rotation (90° around origin)
satisfy *(verb)*	To make an *equation* or *system* of *equations* true. A *solution* to an *equation* or *system of equations* satisfies that *equation* or *system of equations*. (see *solution*)	5 satisfies the equation $2x + 1 = 11$ because $2(5) + 1 = 11$ and $11 = 11$.
segment *(noun)*	*Part* of a *line* between and including two endpoints.	
similar *(adjective)*	Two shapes are similar if corresponding angles have *equal* measures and the ratios of corresponding side lengths are *equivalent*. ~ is the *symbol* for "is similar to." (see *ratio, representation*)	$\triangle ABC \sim \triangle DEF$ because 10:20, 6:12, and 7:14 are equivalent ratios.
simplest form *(noun)*	The form of a *fraction* for which the *numerator* and *denominator* have no common factors other than 1. (see *factor*)	$\dfrac{24}{36} = \dfrac{2}{3}$ simplest form

MATH TERM	MEANING	EXAMPLE
slope *(noun)*	A measure of the steepness of a *line*; the *ratio* of the change in *y* to the change in *x*, often represented by the letter *m*. (see *representation*)	$m = \dfrac{7-4}{7-2} = \dfrac{3}{5}$ (7, 7) (2, 4) 3 5
solution *(noun)*	Any *value* of a *variable* that makes an *equation* true, or any *ordered pair* of values of two variables that makes an *equation* or *system of equations* true. (see *satisfy*)	**y = 5x** x, y, (x, y) 0, 0, (0, 0) 1, 5, (1, 5) 2, 10, (2, 10) 5, 25, (5, 25) *solutions*
speed *(noun)*	How fast something moves; a *ratio* of *distance* to time; a *rate* of *distance* per *unit* of time.	The car travels at a speed of *4* meters per second. *speed*
square number *(noun)*	The *product* of a number and itself; an *expression* raised to an *exponent* of 2. A square number can be represented as the *area* of a square whose side length is the *square root* number of units. (see *representation*, *unit*)	5 5 $5^2 = 5 \cdot 5$ $= 25$ *square number*

MATH TERM	MEANING	EXAMPLE
square root *(noun)*	One of two *equal* factors of a number. The *symbol* for square root is √. The square of any number's square root is the number itself: $(\sqrt{x})^2 = x$ The square root of a *positive* integer that is not a *perfect square* is an *irrational number*. (see *factor*, *integers*, *representation*, *square number*)	5 5 $\sqrt{25} = \sqrt{5 \cdot 5}$ $= 5$ $\sqrt{2} = 1.41421\ldots$
story graph *(noun)*	A *graph* that tells a story of the *motion* of a person or object over time. Usually, time is shown on the *horizontal axis* and *distance* or position is shown on the *vertical axis*. (see *graph*)	B A Distance (m) Time (s)
substitute *(verb)*	To replace a *variable* in an *expression* with a number. We substitute to *evaluate* a *variable expression*.	When $x = -3$ *substitute* $2x + 1 = 2(-3) + 1$ $= -6 + 1$ $= -5$
Substitution Property of Equality *(noun)*	If two expressions are *equal*, then one may be substituted for the other in any *expression* or *equation*. (see *substitute*)	If $x = 2$ and $y = x + 7$, then $y = 2 + 7 = 9$.

MATH TERM	MEANING	EXAMPLE
sum (noun)	The result of addition.	$4 + 8 = \boxed{12}$ sum
symbol (noun)	A *representation*, often a single character, used to replace a word or phrase; symbols often represent operations or relationships. (see *operation*, *variable*)	Common Math Symbols = is equal to > is greater than < is less than + plus − minus × times, multiplication ÷ divided by, division
symmetry (noun)	The property of not changing appearance after a *reflection* or *rotation*. (see *line of symmetry*)	
system of equations (noun)	Two or more equations (with the same variables) considered at the same time. A *solution* of a system of equations makes each *equation* true. An *intersection* of the graphs of a system's equations represents a *solution* to that system. A system of two *linear* equations may have one *solution*, no *solution*, or infinitely many solutions. (see *graph*, *representation*, *variable*)	The system of equations $y = 2x + 8$ $y = -x - 1$ has solution (−3, 2) because $2 = 2(-3) + 8$ and $2 = -(-3) - 1$.

MATH TERM	MEANING	EXAMPLE
table (noun)	A set of numbers or quantities arranged in rows and columns, usually with a header row that describes each column. (see *quantity*)	Time (s) | Distance (m) 1 | 1.5 2 | 3.0 3 | 4.5 4 | 6.0
term (noun)	A term can be a number, a *variable*, or the *product* of numbers and variables. Two terms in an *expression* are separated by a plus sign or a minus sign.	$\boxed{0.5x} + \boxed{3}$ terms
transformation (noun)	A positional change using at least one of the following: *translation* (slide), *reflection* (flip), *rotation* (turn).	Transformation
translation (noun)	A slide *transformation*; a shift in position.	Translation (5 units left)
unit (noun)	A standard of measurement. Each single, *equal*-sized *part* in a bar *model*. (see *area*, *volume*)	12 feet 60 seconds units 24 square centimeters

MATH TERM	MEANING	EXAMPLE
unit price *(noun)*	The cost for one *unit* of an item; the price compared to the *unit* of measurement.	Unit price is $10 per pound.
unit rate *(noun)*	A *rate* that compares two quantities in a way that the second *quantity* is 1 *unit*. Many rates are expressed as *unit* rates.	The rate is 3 tons per hour.
unit ratio *(noun)*	A *ratio* that compares two quantities in a way that either *quantity* is 1 *unit*.	The ratio of shaded to unshaded is 4:1. The ratio of unshaded to shaded is 1:4. unit ratios
unknown *(noun)*	A *quantity* in a math problem that we don't know at first. (see *variable*)	$4 \times 7 =$ ◯ unknown unknown $n + 8 = 12$ $\frac{3}{4} = \frac{\square}{8}$ unknown

	MATH TERM	MEANING	EXAMPLE
V	**value** *(noun)*	The result of evaluating an *expression*. The amount that a digit represents in a multi-digit number. *Variable* quantities have different values in different situations. (see *evaluate*, *quantity*, *representation*)	The value of 5 in 2593 is 500.
	value of ratio *(noun)*	The numeric *value* found by dividing the first number of a *ratio* by the second number of that *ratio*. (see *divide*, *division*)	The value of the ratio 3:4 is 0.75. The value of the ratio 1:8 is $\frac{1}{8}$.
	variable *(noun)*	A letter or *symbol* that represents a *quantity* in an *expression*, *equation*, or *inequality*. (see *constant*)	$d = 3t + 2$ variables
	vertical axis *(noun)*	The *line* on a *graph* that runs straight up and down through the *origin*, often called the *y*-axis. Every *point* on the *y*-axis has an *x-coordinate* of 0. (see *horizontal axis*)	vertical axis

MATH TERM	MEANING	EXAMPLE
volume *(noun)*	The measure of the amount of space inside a solid figure; volume is measured in cubic units; the *formula* for the volume of a rectangular prism is $V = lwh$, where l, w, and h represent length, width, and height. (see *area*, *unit*)	height / width / length $V = lwh$
W		
whole *(noun)*	The total amount; the size of the whole, along with the number of *equal* parts, determines the size of each *part*. In a *percent* problem, the whole corresponds to 100%.	1 whole $\frac{1}{2}$
whole numbers *(noun)*	The counting numbers and zero; {0, 1, 2, 3,…}.	0, 1, 2, 3, . . .
X		
x-intercept *(noun)*	A *point* where a *graph* crosses the *horizontal axis*. 0 is the *y-coordinate* of an *x*-intercept.	x-intercepts

MATH TERM	MEANING	EXAMPLE
Y		
y-intercept *(noun)*	A *point* where a *graph* crosses the *vertical axis*. 0 is the *x*-coordinate of a *y*-intercept. In general, b is the *y*-coordinate of the *y*-intercept of the graph of $y = mx + b$.	y-intercept
Z		
Zero Property of Multiplication *(noun)*	Multiplying any number by 0 results in a *product* of 0. (see *multiplication*, *multiply*)	$8 \cdot 0 = 0$ or $0 \cdot x = 0$

CREDITS

Cover (top to bottom): © Al-xVadinska/Shutterstock, © S_E/Fotolia, © TongRo Images/Thinkstock, © Evryka23/Thinkstock, © Evryka23/Thinkstock, background: © Daniel V Fung/Thinkstock, © Image Source/Getty Images, © MedioImages/Photodisc/Thinkstock, © Minemero/Thinkstock, © prahi/Thinkstock, © Petr Malyshev/Thinkstock, © antipathique/Shutterstock, © Morfous/Dreamstime, cl: © Olga Kovalenko/Shutterstock; **Back Cover** (top to bottom): © Jeffrey Coolidge/Getty Images, © Hero Images/Media Bakery, © Inti St Clair/Getty Images, © Evryka23/Thinkstock, © MedioImages/Photodisc/Thinkstock; p. ii l: © Jeffrey Coolidge/Getty Images, r: © Hero Images/Media Bakery; p. iii l: © Inti St Clair/Getty Images, c: © Evryka23/Thinkstock, r: © MedioImages/Photodisc/Thinkstock; p. 2: © Jeffrey Coolidge/Getty Images; p. 3bl: © 4774344sean/Thinkstock, cl: © Maskot/Getty Images, l: © Kutt Niinepuu/Dreamstime, tr: © Ton Koene/Superstock, cr: © Manuel-F-O/Thinkstock, br: © Jtgarry/Dreamstime, bc: © antipathique/Shutterstock, bl (inset): © KonovalikovAndrey/Thinkstock; p. 5r: Ken Karp © Scholastic Inc.; p. 6l: © Jeffrey Coolidge/Getty Images; pp. 7, 9, 11, 13, 17, 21, 23, 25, 29, 31, 35, 37, 39, 41, 43tr border: © Jeffrey Coolidge/Getty Images; p. 7br: Ken Karp © Scholastic Inc.; p. 14tr: Ken Karp © Scholastic Inc.; p. 17tl: © Iurii Sokolov/Fotolia; p. 19r: Ken Karp © Scholastic Inc.; p. 20tl: © TongRo Images/Thinkstock, tc: © Masterfile (Royalty-Free Division), tr: © Photographerlondon/Dreamstime; p. 21tl: © mediaphotos/iStockphoto, tc: © Wavebreakmedia Ltd/Thinkstock; p. 25br: Ken Karp © Scholastic Inc.; p. 26tr: Ken Karp © Scholastic Inc.; p. 29tl: © Nick Savage/Alamy; p. 33r: Ken Karp © Scholastic Inc.; p. 35br: Ken Karp © Scholastic Inc.; p. 39b: Ken Karp © Scholastic Inc.; p. 42l: © Jeffrey Coolidge/Getty Images, tl: © Fuse/Thinkstock, tr: © Lord_Kuernyus/iStockphoto; p. 44l: © Jeffrey Coolidge/Getty Images, b: Fox 52/Jerchel/Wikimedia Commons; p. 45A tl: © Science Photo Library RF/Getty Images, tr: © Jason Hawkes/Getty Images, b: © Stockbyte/Thinkstock; p. 45B: Kyle Reed © Scholastic Inc.; p. 46: © Hero Images/Media Bakery; p. 47bl: © Chuck Savage/Media Bakery, cl: © ulkan/Thinkstock, c: © nsj-images/Getty Images, t: © Digital Vision/Thinkstock, tr: © Ryan McVay/Thinkstock, cr: © Masterfile, (inset) cr: © Noracarol/Dreamstime, br: © prahi/Thinkstock; p. 49r: Ken Karp © Scholastic Inc.; p. 50l: © Hero Images/Media Bakery; pp. 51, 53, 55, 57, 61, 65, 67, 69, 71, 75, 79, 81, 83, 85, 87tr border: © Hero Images/Media Bakery, br: Ken Karp © Scholastic Inc.; p. 53br: Ken Karp © Scholastic Inc.; p. 58l: Ken Karp © Scholastic Inc.; p. 58c: Jim Kopp © Scholastic Inc.; pp. 59, 60: Jim Kopp © Scholastic Inc.; p. 61tl: © Digital Vision/Thinkstock; p. 63r: Ken Karp © Scholastic Inc.; p. 64 tl: © irina88w/Thinkstock, tc: © John Howard/Getty Images, tr: © Riopatuca/Dreamstime; p. 65tl: © Digital Vision/Getty Images, tc: © Galyna Andrushko/Thinkstock; p. 72tl: Ken Karp © Scholastic Inc., c: Jim Kopp © Scholastic Inc.; pp. 73, 74: Jim Kopp © Scholastic Inc.; p. 75tl: © Masterfile (Royalty-Free Division); p. 77r: Ken Karp © Scholastic Inc.; p. 79br: Ken Karp © Scholastic Inc.; p. 86l: © Hero Images/Media Bakery; p. 86tr: © Poligonchik/Dreamstime; p. 87br: Ken Karp © Scholastic Inc.; p. 88l: © Hero Images/Media Bakery; p. 89A t: © Tim Larsen/AP Images; p. 90: © Inti St Clair/Getty Images; p. 91bl: © Hill Street Studios/Blend Images, cl: © yogesh_more/Thinkstock, tc: © Zero Creatives/Getty Images, tr: © filo/Thinkstock, cr: © Anna Baburkina/Dreamstime, br: © Bryan Faust/Thinkstock, bc: © David H. Lewis/Getty Images,